Why Sit Here
TILL WE DIE

Dicovering
Life in God's Word

Peggy Kirchhoff

By

PEGGY KIRCHHOFF

Ed Kirchhoff
113 Dry Fork Ln
Bonnerdale, AR 71933

Ed 713-591-8594
Peg 713-591-8414

All Scripture quotations are from the authorized King James Version.

WHY SIT HERE TILL WE DIE
Discovering Life in God's Word

ISBN: 0-924748-58-3
UPC: 88571300028-4

Printed in the United States of America
© 2005 by Peggy Kirchhoff

Milestones International Publishers
4410 University Dr., Ste. 113
Huntsville, AL 35816
(256) 536-9402, ext. 234; Fax: (256) 536-4530
www.milestonesintl.com

1 2 3 4 5 6 7 8 9 10 11 / 09 08 07 06 05

DEDICATION

To Eddie, my husband, the wind beneath my wings.

ACKNOWLEDGMENTS

Special thanks to Deborah Lawrence the original story writer. Carol Castro the second author, Ava Siewert proof reader, Lindsay Kirchhoff proof reader, Eli, Tammie, and Elijah Moreno, Mildred Moore, Gaye Blythe, Shanna Hilgers, Tina Menager, Pat Neel, Judy Kingman, Donna Sumpter, (one of the first to work my workbook), Hayden Kirchhoff (one of the first to work my workbook), Opal Ray, Gail Winter, Melody Ferguson, Nancy Watson. Jean Stewart, Majantia Mckean, Emmanuel Baptist Church in Hot Springs Arkansas, Pastor Alan and Shelly Neel, Jewell Holms, My parents Helen and Fred wait, Cleo Pennington. Fred and Nina Kirchhoff, Fred and Faith Kirchhoff, my sisters Joan Salyer, & Kay Lawson, Greg and Donna Turner, Sara Wheeley, Cheryl Every, Sylvia Porter, Anglia Porter, Bill Carter, Paul and Jennifer Struck, Bradley Struck, Haley Struck, Dr. Craig Kirchhoff, Adley Kirchhoff, Kendall Kirchhoff, Dr Phillip Blum, Dr Chris Laveque, Sal Garcia, Billie Housemen, Sandra (nurse Hatchet), Javier, Josea, Jack, and all the people at the blood donor center at the Methodist Hospital in Houston, Anne Vollink Liz Prasek, Eveleen Ward, Francis Chambers, Becky Barton, Life Community Church, Christy Cepato, and many more.

TABLE OF CONTENTS

PREFACE

How powerful is God's Word? Just ask Peggy Kirchhoff. She'll tell you that there's no limit to what it can do for those who are suffering, broken, bitter, depressed, angry, or simply wanting to experience life to the fullest. She will testify that no trial is too great for the God she loves and lives for each new day.

Peggy knows pain. Even more, though, she knows power—the power of God and His mighty Word. That's why her testimony is all the more remarkable. She was given a hopeless diagnosis—a life of pain and perhaps a soon-coming death—but she looked past the pain and found new power. She decided to believe the report of the Lord instead of lean on her own understanding. Today, she's living proof of the miracle-working power of God and His Word.

I encourage you to embrace Peggy's words and to dive headlong into the exciting four-week interactive study she offers to you in this powerful book. Take God at His Word as Peggy chooses to do each new day!

A PERSONAL WORD FROM PEGGY

Do you have the life you've always dreamed of? My guess is that you'll say, "No, Peggy, not really." Few of us do, right?

We all want less pain, suffering, heartache, and trials—and more joy, happiness, love, and blessing, don't we? Somehow, though, life comes at us from a hundred different directions at once and leaves us in a place that looks nothing like the abundant life that Jesus promised us in John 10:10. Simply put, life can be hard.

However, we have a reason for hope! No matter what you're going through today, I have a prescription for your life—God's Word. In the Holy Bible, you will find the Lord's personal message to us. It's a message of hope, healing, love, and life. It can take the most down-and-out person and raise him or her up to soar on wings of eagles! Yes, that's how powerful God's healing Word is.

In the course of my own struggle with a terrible trial of life, God led me down a path that showed me new ways of reading, studying, and meditating on His Word. Some of what He taught me was incredibly different than anything that I had heard before, but I heeded His voice and found a rich storehouse in

His Word that I had never discovered before. Through the Holy Spirit, this method of study truly unleashed the power of God in my life.

Come with me now on a journey that will lead you to the same power in your own life. You'll hear the tragic story of my past, as well as what God is doing in my life today. Then, I'll lead you down the same path that God guided—and still guides—me in the midst of life's trials and tribulations. It's an exciting path, filled with the sweet, healing presence of God. For, along this path, we will immerse ourselves into His very Word to us—the mighty, eternal, and anointed Word of God.

If you're ready to experience a more abundant, more joyful life through God's healing Word, then let's begin our journey together right now!

Peggy Kirchhoff
La Porte, Texas
June, 2005

THE STORY
My Pain, His Power

Then Elisha said, Hear ye the word of the Lord...

2 Kings 7:1

While I was reading God's Word in the peace of my home one night, a cricket's chirp outside the window caught my attention. The familiar sound was a welcome diversion from attempting to overcome my present despair by failing in my efforts to concentrate on God's Word. As the cricket chirped away, I realized that I needed a break. Stopping at 2 Kings 7:1, I dog-eared the page of my Bible and laid it down. As soon as I pulled my hand away from my Bible, I noticed that the cricket had stopped chirping.

Thinking nothing of the cricket's silence, I prepared myself to change positions on my couch, as I was feeling numb. Of course, changing from one position to another was easier said than done. Weakness had become my constant companion. The severity of that weakness increased and diminished seemingly at will. Coming and going without warning, it had a mind of its own. To alleviate the numbness I was feeling, I had to choose the one side that was most comfortable or was the easiest to get to. Clenching my teeth, I squirmed into a more

1

bearable position. There was a little relief, yet the effort had left me drained.

After turning over, I realized how desperate my situation had become. Lying in darkness, except for my reading lamp, I faced the facts. My life had been confined, most of the time, to a six-by-six foot corner of the living room. The couch had become my home: it was my play area, my sleep area, and my dining area. Conveniently, everything that made my tiny home space complete was within reach: a basket overflowing with pills, several versions of the Bible, books and tapes about healing, a phone, a TV remote, a keyboard, and a Janette Oke book that allowed me to escape reality whenever I needed or wanted to. I lived with the realization that, unless God performed a miracle on my behalf, life would never get any better for me. It would, in fact, continue to get worse until it finally came to a bitter end.

HOPE IN HIS WORD

I noticed that the cricket was singing again, and, in the distance, thunder rumbled. I welcomed the thought of listening to a thunderstorm; they could be so savage and satisfying in the Texas Panhandle. I listened for more, yet I heard nothing. Disappointed, I turned back to the Bible. Elisha's words echoed in my mind: *"Hear ye the word of the LORD."* How many times had I asked God for a word? How many times had well-meaning people given me right-sounding words and promises that never seemed to be fulfilled? I was convinced I had to keep hoping—or die. After all, what hope was there except in God? And if there was hope in God, there had to be hope in His Word. I wanted to believe that this word was for me. I longed for anything that I read from God's Word to apply to my life. I wanted to believe that this scripture I was reading right now in this instance was a "special" word just for me. Could God possibly be trying to tell me something important? I prayed for the ability to understand what the Lord had to say. I refocused my eyes with the help of the overhead lamp and began to read again.

> *Thus saith the Lord, To morrow about this time shall a measure of fine flour be sold for a shekel, and two measures of barley for a shekel, in the gate of Samaria. Then a lord on whose hand the king leaned answered the man of God, and said, Behold, if the Lord would make windows in heaven, might this thing be? And he said, Behold, thou shalt see it with thine eyes, but shalt not eat thereof.* (2 Kings 7:1-2)

A bush scraping against the side of the house startled me. The wind was picking up. The sound wasn't the only thing that startled me, however. The scripture I had just read was a burning reminder of the consequences of unbelief. Since I wanted to receive whatever God chose to send me through heaven's window, it was pointless to dwell on the fact that no one seemed to have the answer for my healing. So what if God's Word didn't often appear to speak to my personal circumstances? Does the fact that I wasn't healed mean God didn't want to heal me or couldn't heal me? No! I refused to allow what appeared to be true to interfere with what I knew to be true. In fact, I was afraid *not* to believe.

A few raindrops tapped against the windowpane, giving me hope for a much-needed rainfall that would soothe the dryness of the land. I wished for a few soothing words of hope as well; instead, it seemed that God was pouring out a warning as I remembered what Jesus told the man with the 38-year infirmity. After healing him, Jesus said, *"Sin no more, lest a worse thing come unto thee"* (John 5:14). I remembered once asking God what I had done wrong to deserve having the disease that now ravaged my body. I felt He told me the disease was not a result of sin. The important thing to focus on was not what I had done wrong, but on what Jesus had made right. He had paid the price on the cross for me to have life—and life more abundantly (John 10:10).

LIFE AS AN "OUTCAST"

I was certain my battle was not in the realm of sin, but that of faith. I was determined not to be like the disbelieving king in the passage who was to miss out on God's promised blessing. I noticed that the rain was intensifying. It now drummed steadily against the windowpanes, and the sound was indeed soothing to me. I simply loved storms—still do. As the rain pounded harder outside, I turned the page in my Bible to read the next verse: *"And there were four leprous men..."* (2 Kings 7:3).

Looking up and staring into the dark room, I could practically see the lepers with their white splotches, skin falling off, covered in rags, isolated, and rejected. It wasn't leprosy that kept me trapped on the living room couch day after day. After 20 years of suffering and being misdiagnosed many times, a doctor finally recognized what was wrong with me. It was called Myasthenia Gravis, or M.G., which basically means that I had tremendous muscle weakness. It affected nearly every muscle I had. Aside from not being able to walk or care for myself and my family the way I desired, my inability to chew and swallow properly was probably the most aggravating and frightening of all. When I ate, I had to place my hand under my chin and push up to make my mouth chew. I never knew when I would start choking. Not wanting to make a spectacle of myself, I would often go into another room and eat alone. At times, the only thing I could eat was baby food. The muscles in my face just refused to cooperate. Even my smile was affected. When I tried to smile, a snarl was the result. They even have a name for that part of my illness; it's called an M.G. snarl.

When I was first diagnosed with the disease, I was offered various options and tried many remedies. Almost all of the prescribed drugs exposed me to dangerous side effects. The possibility of getting leukemia, bladder cancer, kidney toxicity, ulcers, and osteoporosis was well explained. Weight gain was also a possibility. I understood all this up front and took the drugs willingly. Even with their potential harm, I welcomed the drugs even for the bit of strength they gave me—and because they were the only answer beside surgery. A particular type of surgery was an option; it was called a thymectomy (the removal of the thymus gland, which can cause temporary or permanent remission for some—but not all). I had been told many horror stories about this procedure. I also had been told that there was no cure for M.G., so I avoided the surgery at all costs and did what I could to survive.

M.G. didn't make me a social outcast as leprosy did for those men in Elisha's time. Sometimes, though, I did feel like a castaway on a deserted island in my own home. Even though I had everything that I needed at my fingertips, no one could really reach me, at least not emotionally. There was no doubt that my husband and children loved me, yet sometimes they seemed worlds apart from me. Even now, in the middle of the night, they were sleeping snug in their beds while I was on the family room couch—my 24-hour home—wide awake and alone. I never intended to burden them with guilt or make them sacrifice their own lives to care for me, although I understood that I had to be a burden to them in my condition. Even knowing this, it would have been nice to have someone around who understood what I was going through. I knew it was unrealistic to hope healthy people could imagine what it was like to lose their ability to live a normal life.

As isolated and alone as I felt sometimes, my couch-home was a haven in comparison to going out in public. Without enough strength to walk, I had to be pushed around in a wheelchair in public. My "pushers," not as conscientious as I would like them to be, bumped my chair into everything possible. Even if it was done accidentally, I soon acquired a fear of stairs and curbs. Laughing out loud, I realized how riding in a wheelchair made me feel. I felt as though I was weighed down with lights and buzzers that screamed out "Danger! Danger! Disease coming through!" If I stayed home, I didn't have to explain my self-conscious feelings—or be consumed with fear that I wouldn't have the strength to tell people my needs. Though the emotional obstacles that kept me from leaving the house seemed larger than life, no one, including myself, appeared able to get over my biggest stumbling block. Beside my couch was my potty chair. It was disguised as a wastebasket, with the hope that no one would notice. When company came over, the "wastebasket" seemed enormous and the center of everyone's focus—at least to me.

Although staying at home meant I didn't have to live in fear of curbs or careless pushers, it was still difficult at times to be trapped inside my own house. I wasn't an outcast, but during the day, I was alone most of the time. Of course, if I fell down or couldn't breathe, or even if I just needed to hear a friendly voice, the phone was within arm's reach. It was a lifeline, strategically placed by my side. Usually, though, no one was around when the thermostat needed resetting to keep me from getting too hot from the steroids I had to take, or to help with meals, or to answer the door, or to let out the dog. And rarely was anyone there to hear when a TV evangelist made me laugh, or when I wanted fellowship, or when my thoughts turned to suicide. I didn't have leprosy, yet I might as well have.

REVELATION DAWNS ON THE HORIZON

I quickly checked my thoughts. I shook my head. How could I have allowed myself to indulge in self-pity? I dried my eyes, even though no one but God was there to see. More than eager for an encouraging word, I began again to read 2 Kings 7:3— *"And there were four leprous men at the entering in of the gate: and they said one to another, Why sit we here until we die?"*

There they were! Inside, my spirit was leaping with joy; outside, I was covered with goose bumps! I knew beyond a shadow of a doubt that God was trying to get my attention. Those words, from His Word, kept repeating themselves over and over in my mind: *"Why sit we here until we die?"* I sensed somehow that God had more in store for me than to just sit on my couch until I died, but I still had no idea what.

I had once heard that people with M.G. were destined to go "from the wheelchair to the bed, and from the bed to the grave." How many times had that thought chipped away at my faith? Now, as the storm thundered outside that night, it was exciting

to have an encouraging thought rolling around in my mind—
"*Why sit we here until we die?*" It made sense not to sit around
and wait to die without trying something. Good health was
going to take a miracle, no doubt about that. Maybe what God
was trying to tell me was that my healing was going to take
action on my part. I struggled to understand as I wiggled into a
more comfortable position. As I did, I realized that revelation
would have to come from God. I kept reading the next verse.

> *If we say, We will enter into the city, then the famine is
> in the city, and we shall die there: and if we sit still
> here, we die also. Now therefore come, and let us fall
> unto the host of Syrians: if they save us alive, we shall
> live; and if they kill us, we shall but die.* (2 Kings 7:4)

Imagine! They were willing to die in order to get relief. Had
I come to that place yet? I had turned everywhere for help—
to my family, doctors, the church, my friends, and even God—
always with the same result: disappointment. Don't get me
wrong—I didn't blame God or anybody else for my situation.
Yet, disappointment still overshadowed me each day. After all,
doctors had told me that I had a good chance of dying, no one
had any answers for me, and I had no insight into what God
was trying to tell me. Disappointment was understandable,
wasn't it? I don't think I was willing to die yet, but I was willing to try just about anything.

A TIME FOR FAITH IN ACTION

I remembered another time, another word, from my younger
days. Then, God had spoken to me from Proverbs. He laid it upon
my heart to take hold of His Word. However, something in my
upbringing made this difficult for me to do. Songs that echoed

sentiments such as, "When the roll is called up yonder, I'll be there," only stirred in me an association of God's Word with death, not life; sadness, not joy. Now, though, He was saying, *"Why sit?"* God seemed to be requiring faith in action on my part. I didn't believe I could earn my healing, but I did believe in obeying the Word of God—like the blind man who was commanded to wash his muddied eyes before being healed (John 9:1–7). So, if God had something for me to do, I was more than willing to do it. As the storm continued to rage outside, I considered that what I really needed was clear direction from God. Was it just a coincidence that there was a storm going on outside as well as inside? It was a storm of revelation and truth stirring up the hope in me that I had long ago buried. Disappointment after disappointment had buried it deep. I knew I had to hear from God, so I kept reading: *"And they rose up in the twilight, to go unto the camp of the Syrians: and when they were come to the uttermost part of the camp of Syria, behold, there was no man there"* (2 Kings 7:5).

The lepers were willing to surrender to the enemy, to give in to whatever happened. They hoped things would get better, not really seeing how they could get much worse. The enemy wasn't even there! God had revealed to the lepers a plan and the actions to take—and look at the results! Maybe it was time for God to reveal His plan for my life. I had tried all that I knew to do and failed. I knew God was the answer. I tried to listen, to hear Him. By now, the storm had died outside, but the newfound silence sounded like a roar in my ears. So, I read on.

For the Lord had made the host of the Syrians to hear a noise of chariots, and a noise of horses, even the noise of a great host: and they said one to another, Lo, the king of Israel hath hired against us the kings of the Hittites, and the kings of the Egyptians, to come upon us. Wherefore they arose and fled in the twilight, and left their tents, and their horses, and their asses, even the camp as it was, and fled for their life. (2 Kings 7:6–7)

The lepers didn't know it, but they had been delivered. While they had decided to simply surrender themselves to the enemy, God was making plans to save them and their town. God had already performed the miracle. Without realizing it, the lepers were experiencing victory. I wondered if that could be true for me too. I knew all things were possible with God. I wondered if perhaps the plan for me to overcome was already in place? I heard the cricket start chirping again and smiled as I read the next verse.

And when these lepers came to the uttermost part of the camp, they went into one tent, and did eat and drink, and carried thence silver, and gold, and raiment, and went and hid it; and came again, and entered into another tent, and carried thence also, and went and hid it. (2 Kings 7:8)

When God does a thing, He does it good! Could I hope for similar results? Complete? Astonishing? The lepers were overcompensated for all that the enemy had stolen from their people. Would I be? How many times had I longed to embrace my children? My husband? But I always lacked the strength to do so. I paused and offered up a silent prayer: *Father, help me to believe You will do it for me also.*

A WORD OF POWER

I felt my eyelids drooping again; it was one of the symptoms of M.G. To make it worse, when I got tired, it was nearly impossible to keep my eyes open all the way. Now was one of those times. Even though reading the Word was exciting and stirring up passions that I thought were dead, it was a struggle for me to continue, but I tried.

Then they said one to another, We do not well: this day is a day of good tidings, and we hold our peace: if we tarry till the morning light, some mischief will come upon us: now therefore come, that we may go and tell the king's household. So they came and called unto the porter of the city: and they told them, saying, We came to the camp of the Syrians, and, behold, there was no man there, neither voice of man, but horses tied, and asses tied, and the tents as they were. And he called the porters; and they told it to the king's house within. And the king arose in the night, and said unto his servants, I will now shew you what the Syrians have done to us. They know that we be hungry; therefore are they gone out of the camp to hide themselves in the field, saying, When they come out of the city, we shall catch them alive, and get into the city. (2 Kings 7:9–12)

The king had assumed his enemies were playing a trick on him. He couldn't imagine that what he was told by the lepers was the truth. I was reminded of my reaction to thinking about having a thymectomy. No matter how many times the surgery was said to be the only answer, I saw that particular solution as a scheme of the enemy. Now, though, I laughed at my constant stubbornness to consider the surgery. Was I being as stubborn as the king? It was time to find God's will in the matter. I prayed again, then kept reading.

11

And one of his servants answered and said, Let some take, I pray thee, five of the horses that remain, which are left in the city, (behold, they are as all the multitude of Israel that are left in it: behold, I say, they are even as all the multitude of the Israelites that are consumed:) and let us send and see. They took therefore two chariot horses; and the king sent after the host of the Syrians, saying, Go and see. And they went after them unto Jordan: and, lo, all the way was full of garments and vessels, which the Syrians had cast away in their haste. And the messengers returned, and told the king. And the people went out, and spoiled the tents of the Syrians. So a measure of fine flour was sold for a shekel, and two measures of barley for a shekel, according to the word of the LORD. (2 Kings 7:13–16)

So, the lepers—the "nobodies"—saved the whole town, all because they decided not to wait and die. Again, I knew better than to make my own plan. As I allowed the cricket's chirp to lull me to sleep, I knew that God had a plan and that it would fulfill His Word. I understood deep in my spirit that my heart's cry would become, "Why sit here until I die?" I didn't know how God would do it, but I knew with every fiber of my being that He was going to bring me through this terrible trial.

As I slipped into a deep slumber, I realized that far too many of God's precious children are sitting around waiting to die. They may not have a life-threatening and incurable disease, but they are believing the lie of the enemy. They believe that they will never get ahead. They believe that they will never achieve their destinies in Christ. The believe that they will never overcome their fear, anger, bitterness, depression, shame, sadness, hopelessness, pain, or a hundred other emotional struggles. They accept the lie of the enemy, and they wallow in their own self-indulged pity. All the while, though, God is reaching out a hand toward them, even as He is working out an unseen plan that will bring them into a new place of experiencing his life-changing power.

It all begins with His Word. In His Word, we find the life and healing power we need to rise above our trials. I drifted away to sleep, content with the knowledge that God was going to work out His perfect plan in my life—and it all began with His Word, the very power for living.

LIFE GOES ON

For I the LORD thy God will hold thy right hand, saying unto thee, Fear not; I will help thee.

Isaiah 41:13

I had been down this road before. The dry and desolate scenery was the same as always. During the 60-minute drive from Pampa to Amarillo, only one place ever showed signs of life. Normally, I enjoyed seeing the farmland "oasis" alongside the road where ducks floated on the water and cattle grazed nearby. The two minutes that it took to pass through the giant stretch of farmland helped console me along my journey through the dry, brown plain known as the Texas Panhandle. This day, though, was different. Nothing could console me, for I was on my way to face one of the biggest fears of my life.

My husband Eddie was driving the luxury van that had become my home away from home. Although I was surrounded by every comfort imaginable, my attention was drawn to and focused on a fly on the ceiling of the van. The

13

fly didn't move, but I knew it could. Still, I hoped it wouldn't because I liked it there. It demanded nothing of me. I could watch the fly without having to perform for it—and that is what my life had become: an act. I had become an expert at putting on a good front for everyone who came to see me in my weakened condition. Like so many of us do when the pain of life gets us down, I hid behind a mask that told the world I was okay—that I was optimistic about the future and didn't concern myself with what I was facing. Really, though, I didn't want anyone to know how fearful I truly was. I had come to trust in the Lord in a new way, but the fear of life still assaulted my mind and spirit daily.

Now, I was on my way to see Dr. Patten in Amarillo. Why? There was only one reason. He was the leading authority on thymectomies. Still, I didn't care what the doctor had to say. I was not having a thymectomy! Hadn't God shown me 60 different scriptures about healing? Hadn't I started making a Bible workbook? Didn't I try my best to memorize the Word of God in order to get it into my spirit? Hadn't I lived for years thinking that, any day now, my miracle would come? I couldn't disappoint God by doubting and settling for a doctor's solution to my problem. However, for Eddie's sake, I agreed to see this doctor, figuring I would just put on a good show, leave unaffected, and then go back to the security of my van with the fly on the ceiling.

FACING THE TRUTH

After we arrived and Dr. Patten heard my history, he looked at me and said, "You are bad. Did you know it?" He turned to Eddie and warned, "If you don't get her some help, she is going to die."

His piercing words squeezed the tears right out of my eyes. I had been in the doctor's presence for only two minutes, and I knew already that I would have a thymectomy—just like the lepers had to face the enemy in 2 Kings.

Please, don't think that the answer God gave me is necessarily the same answer He will give you. The last thing I want to do is influence any major decisions you may have to make. He will speak to you in your circumstance just as He spoke to me in mine—if you are faithful to seek His voice through prayer and reading His Word. Remember, I constantly sought the written and personal word of God. It's important for you to know that on my way home, God confirmed my decision by again giving me the words, *"Why sit we here until we die?"*

God's will was made clear. Before, I had felt like I was settling for something less than God's best. Now, I began to realize that His Word had been bearing fruit in my life like nothing else. No drugs or experimentation had given me the hope I felt at hearing confirmation from God that I was on the right track. I was learning—slowly but surely—that I just needed to be willing to do anything God wanted me to do. That meant even having the surgery I had so long feared.

I flew to Houston one week later. So that I would be strong enough for surgery, I had six plasmaphereses (blood exchanges to remove the excess antibodies that cause M.G.). However, I did not gain much strength because I had an extremely high antibody level. Then came the thymectomy. The surgery was performed on August 13, 1990. Even though I didn't think I would live through it, I did. I felt terrible for months. I was so weak that I thought I might die on any given day. I was given a prognosis of one to two years for remission.

15

My recovery was slow because of my high antibody level. At that time, the highest antibody count that Dr. Patten had heard of was 21,000. My count was at 24,000. Later, it peaked at 64,000. Can I tell you something: I was discouraged! Deep in my spirit, though, I knew I had to keep fighting against what appeared to be true while I held on to what I believed to be true. To battle my doubts and fears, I remained immersed in God's Word. I read it daily. I completed my scripture workbook. I prayed without ceasing.

And God has come through!

LIVING LIFE TO THE FULLEST!

I'm not only still alive, but I've been continually improving over the years. Since February 1993, I have been periodically taking intravenous gamma immune treatments, and that has helped in the physical realm, just as the thymectomy has. Otherwise, God has continued to do a work in my body, but most of all in my spirit—and in my mind. He has transformed me into a woman who will not accept anything less than what He has promised in His Word. Yes, I still have fears and doubts, but they cannot get the best of me because they cannot get the best of my God!

My family has been happy to see the change in my life, too. Before my steady improvement, my son Craig had never known me as anything but diseased. All of my family lived in daily fear of my death. Now, everyone expects me to be around, so my family is able to make plans outside the home that include me. I live an almost normal life now—if you can call it that. I have a very adventuresome family! I have even gone mountain climbing when I couldn't walk (I did a lot of scooting). I also went scuba diving when my mouth was too weak to hold the mouthpiece and my family had to help. They simply wouldn't go anywhere without me!

Yes, I came to the end of myself—and I even lost the drive to serve God. Now, I can see that God used those circumstances to allow His strength to be made perfect in my weakness, as His Word says in 2 Corinthians 12:9. I believe that God has given me a second chance. Armed with the insights and experiences He has given me in life, I can in turn bless them and help them through their trials, no matter how great or small they may seem.

I thank God for transforming my life. What seems unbelievable to me now is remembering that all I wanted to do at Doctor Patten's office was to get back in the van with the fly and go back to the way things were! How glad I am that God took me through the fire even when I wanted to take the easy way out.

What about you? I'll bet life beats you up sometimes. I'll bet you've been through the ringer yourself from time to time. Maybe you even had—or have—it worse than I do. Whatever you've gone through—whatever you're going through—God can make a way for you. It all begins with a word from Him. In His Holy Word, we find His own personal message to us.

So, no matter what you might be going through today, never forget the power that can come from a life lived out of the power of God's Word! According to His Word in Ephesians 1:17–23, I pray this for you:

That the God of our Lord Jesus Christ, the Father of glory, may give unto you the spirit of wisdom and revelation in the knowledge of him: The eyes of your understanding being enlightened; that ye may know what is the hope of his calling, and what the riches of the glory of his inheritance in the saints, and what is the exceeding greatness of his power to us-ward who believe, according to the working of his mighty power, which he wrought in Christ, when he raised him from the dead, and set him at his own right hand in the heavenly places, far above all principality, and power, and might, and dominion, and every name that is named, not only in this world, but also in that which is to come: And hath put all things under his feet, and gave him to be the head over all things to the church, which is his body, the fulness of him that filleth all in all.

Amen!

~~ ❀ ~~

THE STUDY

Don't Forget Your Daily Dose!

For thus saith the LORD, Thy bruise is incurable, and thy wound is grievous. There is none to plead thy cause, that thou mayest be bound up: thou hast no healing medicines. All thy lovers have forgotten thee; they seek thee not; for I have wounded thee with the wound of an enemy, with the chastisement of a cruel one, for the multitude of thine iniquity; because thy sins were increased. Why criest thou for thine afflic-tion? thy sorrow is incurable for the multitude of thine iniquity: because thy sins were increased, I have done these things unto thee. Therefore all they that devour thee shall be devoured; and all thine adversaries, every one of them, shall go into captivity; and they that spoil thee shall be a spoil, and all that prey upon thee will I give for a prey. For I will restore health unto thee, and I will heal thee of thy wounds, saith the LORD; because they called thee an Outcast, saying, This is Zion, whom no man seeketh after.

Jeremiah 30:12–17

"*Thou hast no healing medicines.*" I woke up in a cold sweat. I gasped for air. My eyes darted about in the bedroom's darkness. My mind was racing. My medicine!

I screamed inside, barely keeping the panic to myself. I forgot to take my medicine! My heart felt heavy and was beating wildly. Was I dying? I replayed the day's schedule in my mind. Had I taken my medicine? Maybe it had been days since I had remembered to take it. I was frantic as I thought about all the things that could happen to me if I had forgotten. Some of the drugs were extremely dangerous. If I wasn't consistent, I could die. When? When did I take it? Lord, help me! I went over and over in my mind and finally remembered. Yes! I was certain I had taken the pills just as prescribed. Peace washed over me. I could finally let loose a big sigh.

Soon, a memory crept back from last night and the week before—and the week before that. For many nights, I had been dreaming the same dream over and over—that I had forgotten to take my medicine. What did that mean? Ah, it was falling into place now. Yes, I had taken my medicine—my physical medicine. But the dream had greater significance than that. Where was the healing medicine for my spirit? I realized I hadn't read the Bible lately!

I certainly had good intentions of reading the Word daily. I even went so far as to put scriptures inside of a pill bottle and promise myself that when I took my daily medicine, I would also take a "dose" of God's medicine. Once, I had even made myself a scripture bracelet to help remind me of the Word that I wanted to apply that day. Now, though, I was having trouble with consistency, and God was reminding me through my dreams—which had nightmarish possibilities.

At first, I searched the bookstore aisles trying to find just the right book to give me the key to the healing I so desperately needed. Then, I finally realized it was the Bible—God's living Holy Word—that I needed to be set free. The Word of God is so important! His Word says in Hosea 4:6, *"My people are destroyed for lack of knowledge."* So, I wanted knowledge, but not just any knowledge. I had to get life-giving knowledge (John 1:1; 1:14; 14:6). That is the reason I sought God and wanted His Word in me. I didn't know how to put God's Word to work in my life, however. I needed a plan, so I prayed—and God gave me a plan! The plan was simple, and I soon found that it was working!

As time went on, I discovered exciting ways to learn the Word and developed a 15-minute-a-day program. When I first had the idea to write down the daily plan, I thought it was too simple to share in a book. Yet, I knew it had worked for me, and maybe it could work for others. So, I reasoned that others might be interested in what I had found. Besides, I couldn't forget the lepers. Hadn't they also felt convicted because they were not sharing what God have given them in the midst of their trial?

I knew firsthand about the frustration of trying to dig into God's Word when I so desperately needed it. My prayer is that my experience in studying God's Word will benefit those who are desperate to get His Word into their hearts and spirits. The Bible study workbook that follows is the material I would like to have found already being sold in the bookstores, but I had to write it myself because nothing like it was available.

From the leper story in 2 Kings, I knew I didn't want to sit around waiting to die. So, I got into action and combined the need for God's Word in my life with my need for health. I searched the scriptures to find out what God had to say about healing. I also knew I needed a structured book to teach me the Word as I studied it, and that is why this book is written in workbook form. Memorizing scripture, as essential as it was, got boring, so I made up games to help me learn. I learned 60 healing scriptures by repeatedly listening to a healing tape and discovered the importance of meditating on the Word. I've read that *"Out of the abundance of the heart the mouth speaketh"* (Matthew 12:34). This is why writing, hearing, and speaking the word are emphasized in this study.

My struggles in learning how to get into the Word have culminated in the workbook you are about to begin. Whatever you're facing in life—bitterness, anger, shame, pain, suffering, or even a terrible disease—you can be assured that this workbook will do a work in your heart and spirit. Never forget the words of Isaiah 55:10–11:

> *For as the rain cometh down, and the snow from heaven, and returneth not thither, but watereth the earth, and maketh it bring forth and bud, that it may give seed to the sower, and bread to the eater: So shall my word be that goeth forth out of my mouth: it shall not return unto me void, but it shall accomplish that which I please, and it shall prosper in the thing whereto I sent it.*

Pray to the Lord and ask His Spirit to do a mighty work in your own life as you work your way through this study. As it says in Zechariah 4:6, it is *"not by might, nor by power, but by my spirit, saith the Lord of hosts."*

GETTING THE MOST OUT OF HIS WORD

Study to shew thyself approved unto God, a workman that needeth not to be ashamed, rightly dividing the word of truth.

2 Timothy 2:15

You can learn anything in one of three ways: kinetic (doing and writing), auditory (hearing), and visual (seeing). These three are incorporated throughout this study and will reinforce the teaching presented. Each day while working through this 28-day workbook, you will learn a new scripture and then go through exercises with activities that use the verse you have learned.

The first week's scriptures will concentrate on the Word and how it heals. When we speak the Word, we speak the truth. Scriptures for the second week pertain to the cross. The cross is where we face the truth about the Word. The subject for the third week is the mind and mouth. The mind is where our battles begin, and our mouths are where we have the power to overcome every battle. Faith and fear are the themes for the fourth and final week. Faith is the shield by which we face our fears. We can learn to overcome the negative influence of fear if we learn to stand in faith and fear only Him who has the keys of hell and death.

Each step of every day's work is vital to the successful completion of the workbook. Every day, you will learn a new scripture, complete the exercises, pray, and take your healing medicine.

Later, when you have completed the workbook, you can start all over and redo it as many times as you like (if you plan to do this, you might use a pencil rather than a pen).

The directions for completing this study are simple:

• Complete material in order

• Testing every seven days

• Healing medicine found at the end of each chapter

• You will need these tools: pencil or pen, and a King James Bible (all scriptures are in King James Version)

Some exercises and steps may seem insignificant, even odd. But remember—it is repetition that drives wisdom and insight into our souls and spirits. In the military, soldiers repeat the same movements a thousand times until it becomes second nature. In this way, they are ready to respond in times of combat, when the pressure is intense and the enemy is before them. So it is with us, fellow warriors in the Lord. Our enemy is always before us, trying to assault us physically, mentally, and spiritually. However, if you have placed God's Word deep in your heart and it is now second nature to trust in Him rather than what your circumstances are saying, you will stand in the *"evil day"* that the Apostle Paul spoke of in Ephesians 6:13. You will find yourself able to overcome the negative feelings and emotions that try to drag you down. You will rise above depression, bitterness, and anger. And you will find healing in Him. But—it all starts with immersing yourself in God's Word. To live in the power of His Word, you must first choose to live in His Word.

Week One

THE WORD

꒫꒿꒭

LAYING A SOLID FOUNDATION

As you work your way through this study, please know that I have been where you are today. I searched the scriptures to find what I thought would be the answer to my own struggles in life. At first, I didn't have you in mind. As time passed, I knew that the truth God had revealed to me would benefit others as well. So, let's start at the beginning. I would like for you to write down some things you know about healing: scriptures, stories, truth or lie. Just be honest. We will do this exercise again at the end of the workbook.

_____

_____

_____

_____

_____

Now, forget about everything you just wrote (for now). We are going to take a fresh look at healing. God sent His Word and healed us. That Word is Jesus, and, as you work through this study, you will daily learn how to use the Word to set you free from whatever you are facing. You will learn how to plant a garden of healing words that can be harvested as needed for yourself or others. This is the workbook I looked for, never found, and had to make. This workbook could hold the key for your own personal healing. May God give you wisdom as you continue in his word. God's Word says, *"If ye continue in my word, then are ye my disciples indeed; and ye shall know the truth, and the truth shall make you free"* (John 8:31–32). So, let's get to work on your garden on Day One!

RECITING TODAY'S SCRIPTURE

Slowly, say out loud three times ...

Matthew 4:4

It is written, Man shall not live by bread alone, but by every word that proceedeth out of the mouth of God.

FILL IN THE BLANKS

1. Matthew 4:4—_____ is _____,
man _____ not _____ by _____
alone, _____ by _____ word _____
proceedeth _____ of _____
mouth _____ God.

2. _____—It _____ written, _____
shall _____ live _____
bread _____, but _____
every _____ that _____
out _____ the _____ of _____.

3. Matthew 4:4—It is written, man shall not live by bread alone,
_____.

4. Matthew 4:4—_____,
but by every word that proceedeth out of the mouth of God.

5. _____—It is written, man shall not live by bread
alone, but by every word that proceedeth out of the mouth of
God.

6. Matthew 4:4—_____

_____.

READ IT IN THE BIBLE

Find and read Matthew 4:4 in your Bible.

WORD PUZZLE

Circle the hidden words in the puzzle below. Words may
appear diagonally, vertically, horizontally, or backwards. Work
puzzle in order as scripture is written here:

*It is written, Man shall not live by bread alone, but by
every word that proceedeth out of the mouth of God.*

```
S  H  A  L  L  D  F  R  B  Y  T
F  M  A  N  W  O  R  D  R  B  A
T  O  D  Y  E  G  E  E  O  U  C
A  U  R  A  V  R  V  N  T  H  Y
H  T  E  D  E  E  C  O  R  P  R
T  H  H  A  L  R  N  L  I  V  E
O  U  T  S  T  U  B  A  V  O  V
W  R  I  T  T  E  N  M  A  M  E
```

SAY THE WORD SCRAMBLE

Recite today's scripture again. As you do, cross off each of the words as they appear in the list below.

is but that out the shall Matthew 4:4 of alone, man written, proceedeth not of live every by word It bread God by mouth

PRAYING FROM GOD'S WORD

Pray this prayer out of God's Word.

Father, in Jesus' name, I thank you that your words are life to me, and that you sent your word and healed me. Forever, O Lord, your word is settled in heaven. Amen.

(Philippians 2:10; Psalm 107:20)

YOUR THOUGHTS ON TODAY'S WORD

In the space below, write down what you have learned today as you meditate and dwell on our memory scripture.

_____
_____
_____
_____
_____
_____

EXTRA DAILY BIBLE READING

For an extra dose of God's Word, read John 1:1–7.

HEALING MEDICINE

Read the Healing Medicine that appears at the end of this chapter now and at least twice more today.

NOTES

_____

_____

_____

_____

_____

_____

_____

_____

_____

DAY   2

∿⁂∿

PLANTING
POWERFUL SEEDS

As the Word says, *"Man does not live by bread alone but by every word that proceedeth out of the mouth of God"* (Matt.4:4). The Word of God is our healer. I've watched different healing ministries for years, and many are good. Yet, many people are not healed and are very disappointed. I believe what Mark 4 says, that our gardens have no seed (word). Your garden may be plowed and ready, but you forgot to plant the seed. The seed is the word, and a garden will not grow without seed. You need the right seed (word). You can't plant peas and get corn.

However, you have to get the right word—a healing word. This workbook will help plant the right seeds in your garden. Then, as you continue in the Word and continue working these healing exercises, you will learn how to nurture and harvest your garden. Some will receive a 30-fold, 60-fold, or even a 100-fold return. You will also, in time, learn how to help others plant their gardens. THE KINGDOM OF GOD IS SET UP ON SEEDTIME AND HARVEST!

> *"And he said unto them, Unto you is given to know the mystery of the kingdom of God: but unto them that are without, all these things are done in parables."* (Mark

31

4:11). As you work this study today, you are starting the process of planting your healing garden. So, lets get started planting those seeds.

RECITING TODAY'S SCRIPTURE

Slowly, say out loud three times ...

Proverbs 4:20

My son, attend to my words; incline thine ear unto my sayings.

FILL IN THE BLANKS

1. Proverbs 4:20—_____ son, _____ to _____ words; _____ thine _____ unto _____ sayings.

2. _____—My _____, attend _____ my _____; incline _____ ear _____ my _____.

3. Proverbs 4:20—My son, attend to my words; _____.

4. Proverbs 4:20 _____; incline thine ear unto my sayings.

5. _____—My son, attend to my words; incline thine ear unto my sayings.

6. Proverbs 4:20—_____.

READ IT IN THE BIBLE

Find and read Proverbs 4:20 in your Bible.

WORD PUZZLE

Circle the hidden words in the puzzle below. Words may appear diagonally, vertically, horizontally, or backwards. Work puzzle in order as scripture is written here:

My son, attend to my words; incline thine ear unto my sayings.

```
I  N  W  O  R  D  S
N  D  N  E  T  T  A
C  L  T  O  H  M  Y
L  E  A  R  I  S  I
I  N  Y  A  N  O  N
N  A  M  Y  E  N  G
E  Q  U  N  T  O  S
```

SAY THE WORD SCRAMBLE

Recite today's scripture again. As you do, cross off each of the words as they appear in the list below.

attend ear sayings. words; incline my thine unto My Proverbs 4:20 son, my to

PRAYING FROM GOD'S WORD

Pray this prayer out of God's Word, then wait on God to hear what He has to say to you. Use the space below to write what you hear.

Father, in Jesus' name, you say that if I call on you that you will answer and show me great and mighty things that I know not. I am calling on you for instruction from the Holy Spirit for my life and my healing. Give me your wisdom. Amen.

(Jeremiah 33:3; Philippians 2:10; Psalm 32:8)

_____

_____

_____

_____

_____

_____

_____

YOUR THOUGHTS ON TODAY'S WORD

In the space below, write down what you have learned today as you meditate and dwell on our memory scripture.

_____

_____

_____

_____

_____

_____

EXTRA DAILY BIBLE READING

For an extra dose of God's Word, read Mark 4:14–20.

HEALING MEDICINE

Read the Healing Medicine that appears at the end of this chapter now and at least twice more today.

NOTES

_____

_____

_____

_____

_____

_____

_____

_____

_____

_____

PLANTING DAY BY DAY

When I was a little girl growing up in Arkansas, I remember helping my Daddy in the garden. The smell of newly turned black soil and the big horse pulling the plow are still a part of my memory today. My plan was to work hard all day long, helping my Daddy and making him happy. My intentions were good, even though my energy didn't last long. So, let's try to do better than I did in our old garden. I don't know what picture this paints in your mind or what you know about planting a garden. But remember that, as we work this workbook, we are planting our seeds (the Word) in our gardens (our hearts).

RECITING TODAY'S SCRIPTURE

Slowly, say out loud three times ...

Proverbs 4:21

Let them not depart from thine eyes; keep them in the midst of thine heart.

FILL IN THE BLANKS

1. Proverbs 4:21—_____ them _____
depart _____ thine _____; keep

_____ in _____ midst _____ thine

_____.

2. _____—Let _____ not _____
from _____ eyes; _____ them
_____ the _____ of _____ heart.

3. Proverbs 4:21 Let them not depart from thine eyes;

_____.

4. Proverbs 4:21—_____; keep them in the midst of
thine heart.

5. _____—Let them not depart from thine eyes;
keep them in the midst of thine heart.

6. Proverbs 4:21—_____

_____.

READ IT IN THE BIBLE

Find and read Proverbs 4:21 in your Bible.

WORD PUZZLE

Circle the hidden words in the puzzle below. Words may appear diagonally, vertically, horizontally, or backwards. Work puzzle in order as scripture is written here:

Let them not depart from thine eyes; keep them in the midst of thine heart.

```
M  I  D  S  T  H  E  M
O  M  E  E  H  E  I  E
R  E  P  Y  I  N  P  H
F  H  A  E  N  I  E  T
O  T  R  A  E  H  E  T
L  E  T  N  O  T  K  H
```

SAY THE WORD SCRAMBLE

Recite today's scripture again. As you do, cross off each of the words as they appear in the list below.

depart keep the thine Let heart. midst thine eyes; them them Proverbs 4:21 in from not of

PRAYING FROM GOD'S WORD

Pray for someone else right now, remembering that James 5:16 says, *"Pray one for another, that ye may be healed."*

YOUR THOUGHTS ON TODAY'S WORD

In the space below, write down what you have learned today as you meditate and dwell on our memory scripture.

EXTRA DAILY BIBLE READING

For an extra dose of God's Word, read Psalm 119:1–40.

HEALING MEDICINE

Read the Healing Medicine that appears at the end of this chapter now and at least twice more today.

NOTES

_____

_____

_____

_____

_____

_____

_____

_____

_____

_____

❧

KEEP DIGGING

Mary, Mary, quite contrary, how does your garden grow? In Mark 4, God's Word says that Satan comes immediately to steal the word. Why do we want to keep planting the Word? If we keep planting, we will reap a crop—if we faint not. And trust me—it's worth all the hard work and the wait! So keep planting!

RECITING TODAY'S SCRIPTURE

Slowly, say out loud three times …

Proverbs 4:22

For they are life unto those that find them, and health to all their flesh.

FILL IN THE BLANKS

1. Proverbs 4:22—_____ they _____ life _____ those _____ find _____, and _____ to _____ their _____.

2. _____—For _____ are _____ unto _____ that _____ them, _____ health _____ all _____ flesh.

3. Proverbs 4:22—For they are life unto those that find them,

_____.

4. Proverbs 4:22—_____, and health to all their flesh.

5. _____—For they are life unto those that find them, and health to all their flesh.

6. Proverbs 4:22—_____

_____.

READ IT IN THE BIBLE

Find and read Proverbs 4:22 in your Bible.

WORD PUZZLE

Circle the hidden words in the puzzle below. Words may appear diagonally, vertically, horizontally, or backwards. Work puzzle in order as scripture is written here:

For they are life unto those that find them, and health to all their flesh.

```
P A N D Y O T N U
O N T H E T H E M
D H E S H H I T D
L N E E T H O S E
I L I L O H F H R
F D A F O R A C A
E E T H E I R T S
H G D L L A O B R
```

SAY THE WORD SCRAMBLE

Recite today's scripture again. As you do, cross off each of the words as they appear in the list below.

flesh to health and them, find that all those their unto life are they For Proverbs 4:22

PRAYING FROM GOD'S WORD

Pray this prayer out of God's Word.

Father, in Jesus' name, I thank you that your words are life to me, and health to all my flesh. Help me to continue in your word. Strengthen thou me according unto thy word. Amen.

(Philippians 2:10; Proverbs 4:22; John 8:31; Psalm 119:28)

YOUR THOUGHTS ON TODAY'S WORD

In the space below, write down what you have learned today as you meditate and dwell on our memory scripture.

_____

_____

_____

_____

_____

_____

_____

_____

_____

EXTRA DAILY BIBLE READING

For an extra dose of God's Word, read Psalm 119:41–80.

HEALING MEDICINE

Read the Healing Medicine that appears at the end of this chapter now and at least twice more today.

NOTES

_____

_____

_____

_____

_____

_____

_____

_____

_____

_____

STANDING ON THE TRUTH

As I have said before, the Kingdom of God is based on the principle of seedtime and harvest. We have been learning about planting seeds, and now we are going to learn about what happens when the Word—your seed—is sown. In Day 2's Extra Daily Bible Reading, you read Mark 4:14–20. Did you notice how many times the word "immediately" appears? Anytime the Word is sown, Satan comes IMMEDIATELY to steal the word. Every time we learn a little word of truth, the enemy comes to steal it away. *"The thief cometh not, but for to steal, and to kill, and to destroy: I am come that they might have life, and that they might have it more abundantly"* (John 10:10). Keep planting those seeds and eventually they have to grow. God's Word does not return void. *"So shall my word be that goeth forth out of my mouth: it shall not return unto me void, but it shall accomplish that which I please and it shall prosper in the thing whereto I sent it"* (Isaiah 55:11). Keep planting!

RECITING TODAY'S SCRIPTURE

Slowly, say out loud three times ...

John 17:17

Thy word is truth.

Day 5

FILL IN THE BLANKS

1. John 17:17—_Thy_ word _is_ truth.

2. _John 17:17_ —Thy _Word_ is _truth_.

3. John 17:17—Thy word _is truth_.

4. John 17:17—_Thy Word_ is truth.

5. _Joh 17:17_ —Thy word is truth.

6. John 17:17—_Thy word is truth_.

READ IT IN THE BIBLE

Find and read John 17:17 in your Bible.

WORD PUZZLE

Circle the hidden words in the puzzle below. Words may appear diagonally, vertically, horizontally, or backwards. Work puzzle in order as scripture is written here:

Thy word is truth.

```
T O P B I
D R L S M
R N U J K
O Y H T G
W U Y D H
```

SAY THE WORD SCRAMBLE

Recite today's scripture again. As you do, cross off each of the words as they appear in the list below.

truth John 17:17 word is thy

PRAYING FROM GOD'S WORD

Write in your own words your prayer from God's Word.

_____

_____

_____

_____

_____

_____

YOUR THOUGHTS ON TODAY'S WORD

In the space below, write down what you have learned today as you meditate and dwell on our memory scripture.

_____

_____

_____

_____

_____

_____

EXTRA DAILY BIBLE READING

For an extra dose of God's Word, read Psalm 119:81–120.

HEALING MEDICINE

Read the Healing Medicine that appears at the end of this chapter now and at least twice more today.

NOTES

_____

_____

_____

_____

_____

_____

_____

_____

_____

DAY 6

.ﾟ.ﾟ.

FINDING FREEDOM

M ark 4 says that the mystery of the Kingdom of God is set
upon the principle of seedtime and harvest. We have
previously talked about how we are planting seeds as we are
learning these healing scriptures. We have also learned that
Satan comes immediately to steal the word when it is planted. Today, let's examine what kind of soil you have. My mother grows some of the best vegetables and the prettiest flowers
and plants. She makes sure that she is always tilling and
adding to her soil. She gives a lot of attention to her garden—
and it shows. Mark 4 says that there are three types of ground:
stony ground, ground among thorns, and good ground. What
kind of ground do you have? In other words, what comes out
of your mouth when something bad happens to you? Do you
call on God's name or do you curse his name? "*Out of the
abundance of the heart the mouth speaks*" (Luke 6:45). Your
mouth will tell on you! "*Out of the same mouth proceedeth
blessing and cursing. My brethren, these things ought not so
to be. Doth a fountain send forth at the same place sweet
water and bitter*" (James 3:10-11). Your mouth usually
reveals your heart, but you can change your heart and your
mouth with the Lord's help.

48

RECITING TODAY'S SCRIPTURE

Slowly, say out loud three times ...

John 8:32

And ye shall know the truth, and the truth shall make you free.

FILL IN THE BLANKS

1. John 8:32—_____ ye _____ know _____ truth, _____ the _____ shall _____ you _____.

2. _____—And _____ shall _____ the _____, and _____ truth _____ make _____ free.

3. John 8:32—And ye shall know the truth, _____.

4. John 8:32—_____, and the truth shall make you free.

5. _____—And ye shall know the truth, and the truth shall make you free.

6. John 8:32—

_____

_____.

READ IT IN THE BIBLE

Find and read John 8:32 in your Bible.

WORD PUZZLE

Circle the hidden words in the puzzle below. Words may appear diagonally, vertically, horizontally, or backwards. Work puzzle in order as scripture is written here:

And ye shall know the truth, and the truth shall make you free.

```
P  T  L  L  A  H  S  B
S  H  R  N  T  D  H  W
F  E  D  U  O  Y  A  O
R  H  R  F  T  K  L  N
E  T  H  E  Y  H  L  K
E  K  A  M  T  D  N  A
```

SAY THE WORD SCRAMBLE

Recite today's scripture again. As you do, cross off each of the words as they appear in the list below.

shall And make free and know the truth you shall John 8:32 ye truth, the

PRAYING FROM GOD'S WORD

Pray this prayer out of God's Word.

Father, in Jesus' name, thank you that your word is true, and that your word is my healer. It is a lamp

unto my feet and a light unto my path. I trust in your
word. Amen.

(Psalm 119:105)

YOUR THOUGHTS ON TODAY'S WORD

In the space below, write down what you have learned
today as you meditate and dwell on our memory scripture.

_____

_____

_____

_____

_____

EXTRA DAILY BIBLE READING

For an extra dose of God's Word, read Psalm
119:121–176.

HEALING MEDICINE

Read the Healing Medicine that appears at the end of this
chapter now and at least twice more today.

NOTES

_____

_____

_____

_____

_____

GET KNOWLEDGE

God's Word says that we are destroyed for lack of knowledge (Hosea 4:6). We know that this is true because God is not a man that He should lie. This means that we must get knowledge, although not just any knowledge. We need the right knowledge—true knowledge, Bible knowledge. Acquiring and applying the right scripture is very important. According to the law of seedtime and harvest, we must plant seed—the right seed—in order to have a harvest. Several years ago, I would be the first person to tell you that God could heal you. However, I could not tell you where in the Bible to find these scriptures. I thought I had a garden planted. I soon discovered it was void of seed. I was almost too weary and weak when I started searching for these scriptures. Now I've got a crop, and I would like to share it with you. My mother and father taught me the blessings that come from sharing. They share their vegetables, their garden, and anything else that they have. You just don't leave their house empty-handed. I want you to feel the same way every time you work on this workbook. I would like for you to feel as though you have come away with another gift. Keep planting the right word!

RECITING TODAY'S SCRIPTURE

Slowly, say out loud three times …

Hosea 4:6

My people are destroyed for lack of knowledge.

FILL IN THE BLANKS

1. Hosea 4:6—_____ *My* _____ people _____ *Are* _____
destroyed _____ *for* _____ lack _____ *of* _____ knowledge.

2. _*Hosea 4:6*_ —My _____ *people* _____ are _*destroyed*_
for _____ *Lack* _____ of _*knowledge*_ .

3. Hosea 4:6— My people are destroyed _*for Lack of Knowledge*_

4. Hosea 4:6—_*My people Are destroyed*_ for lack of knowledge.

5. _*Hosea 4:6*_ —My people are destroyed for lack of
knowledge.

6. Hosea 4:6— _*My people Are destroyed for Lack*_
*of Knowledge.* .

READ IT IN THE BIBLE

Find and read Hosea 4:6 in your Bible.

WORD PUZZLE

Circle the hidden words in the puzzle below. Words may appear diagonally, vertically, horizontally, or backwards. Work puzzle in order as scripture is written here:

My people are destroyed for lack of knowledge.

SAY THE WORD SCRAMBLE

Recite today's scripture again. As you do, cross off each of the words as they appear in the list below.

people knowledge for destroyed Hosea 4:6 lack of My are

PRAYING FROM GOD'S WORD

Pray this prayer out of God's Word, then wait on God to hear what He has to say to you. Use the space below to write what you hear.

Father, in Jesus' name, you say that if I call on you that you will answer and show me great and mighty things that I know not. I am calling on you for instruction from the Holy Spirit for my life and my healing. Give me your wisdom. Amen.

(Jeremiah 33:3; Philippians 2:10; Psalm 32:8)

_____

_____

_____

YOUR THOUGHTS ON TODAY'S WORD

In the space below, write down what you have learned today as you meditate and dwell on our memory scripture.

_____

_____

_____

_____

- -

EXTRA DAILY BIBLE READING

For an extra dose of God's Word, read Proverbs 4:1–27.

HEALING MEDICINE

Read the Healing Medicine that appears at the end of this chapter now and at least twice more today.

TEST TIME

Take the test located after this chapter's Healing Medicine.

NOTES

_____

_____

_____

_____

_____

_____

WEEK ONE HEALING MEDICINE

Matthew 4:4—*It is written, Man shall not live by bread alone, but by every word that proceedeth out of the mouth of God.*

Proverbs 4:20—*My son, attend to my words; incline thine ear unto my sayings.*

Proverbs 4:21—*Let them not depart from thine eyes; keep them in the midst of thine heart.*

Proverbs 4:22—*For they are life unto those that find them, and health to all their flesh.*

John 17:17—*Thy word is truth.*

John 8:32—*And ye shall know the truth, and the truth shall make you free.*

Hosea 4:6—*My people are destroyed for lack of knowledge.*

WEEK ONE TEST

Fill In The Blanks

_____—It is written, Man shall not live by bread alone, but by every word that proceedeth out of the mouth of God.

_____—My son, attend to my words; incline thine ear unto my sayings.

_____—Let them not depart from thine eyes; keep them in the midst of thine heart.

_____—For they are life unto those that find them, and health to all their flesh.

_____—Thy word is truth.

_____—And ye shall know the truth, and the truth shall make you free.

_____—My people are destroyed for lack of knowledge.

Matthew 4:4—_____

Proverbs 4:20—_____

Proverbs 4:21—_____

Proverbs 4:22—_____

John 17:17—_____

John 8:32—_____

Hosea 4:6—_____

Week Two

THE CROSS

DAY 8

POWER IN THE BLOOD

We are now entering "Week 2: The Cross." We will learn about the cross and what the blood of Christ has done for us. Keep in mind that we are still planting seeds. There are many ways to plant seeds. Right now, we are concentrating on getting the right word into our heart and mind. This workbook is one way of planting the word (seed).

Now, back to the cross. I was raised in the Pentecostal church, and I didn't even know what the blood of Jesus had done for me until I had a very dramatic dream. We lived in Pampa, Texas. We were visiting relatives at a family reunion in Comfort, in the hill country of Texas. First, I dreamt that I died and I was climbing stairs. They were ugly. The carpet was torn. Yet, the higher I climbed, the more beautiful they became. I wanted to climb the ornate stairs faster to get to the top. When I reached the top, I saw a waterfall flowing blood red. The water-fall had a face. It spoke to me; it said, "I'm the Blood of Jesus." At that time, I started the quest of finding out what the blood had done for me (I'll tell you more about the dream later).

I want to talk about the cross and explain the blood of Jesus Christ to you. It has an endless supply and never will run out—and we should share it. It was shed equally for me and for you. It saves us from our sins and heals us of our dis-eases. Another time, I had a vision of Jesus on a cross with his blood flowing into a red river that washed away sin and sickness. I have never had many dreams or visions. The ones that I have had were very dramatic. Don't forget—as you are learning about the cross that you are actually planting seeds.

RECITING TODAY'S SCRIPTURE

Slowly, say out loud three times ...

Psalm 107:20

He sent his word, and healed them, and delivered them from their destructions.

FILL IN THE BLANKS

1. Psalm 107:20—_____ sent _____ word, _____ healed _____, and _____ them _____ their _____.

2. _____—He _____ his _____, and _____ them, _____ delivered _____ from _____ destructions.

3. Psalm 107:20—He sent his word, and healed them, _____.

4. Psalm 107:20—_____, and delivered them from their destructions.

5. _____—He sent his word, and healed them, and delivered them from their destructions.

6. Psalm 107:20—_____

_____.

READ IT IN THE BIBLE

Find and read Psalm 107:20 in your Bible.

WORD PUZZLE

Circle the hidden words in the puzzle below. Words may appear diagonally, vertically, horizontally, or backwards. Work puzzle in order as scripture is written here:

He sent his word, and healed them, and delivered them from their destructions.

```
S  I  H  F  W  Y  K  M  L
N  Y  S  R  O  X  W  L  E
O  W  R  O  R  W  T  A  K
I  O  L  M  D  K  S  G  C
T  H  E  M  A  J  P  P  A
C  F  M  M  R  G  N  D  B
U  E  J  M  Q  R  A  E  R
R  R  I  E  H  T  E  L  D
T  S  I  H  J  D  H  A  N
S  E  N  T  L  B  J  E  A
E  L  C  K  A  A  L  H  N
D  E  L  I  V  E  R  E  D
```

SAY THE WORD SCRAMBLE

Recite today's scripture again. As you do, cross off each of the words as they appear in the list below.

Word, his and them, and Psalms 107:20 He healed delivered their from sent them destructions

PRAYING FROM GOD'S WORD

Pray this prayer out of God's Word.

Father, in Jesus' name, I thank you that you sent your son (Jesus), and healed me, and delivered me from my destruction. Amen.

(Philippians 2:10; Psalm 107:20)

YOUR THOUGHTS ON TODAY'S WORD

In the space below, write down what you have learned today as you meditate and dwell on our memory scripture.

_____

_____

_____

_____

_____

EXTRA DAILY BIBLE READING

For an extra dose of God's Word, read 1 John 1:1–10.

HEALING MEDICINE

Read the Healing Medicine that appears at the end of this chapter now and at least twice more today.

NOTES

_____

_____

_____

_____

_____

_____

_____

_____

_____

_____

_____

THE SUFFERING SERVANT

I promised you that I would tell you more about the dream about Christ's blood. This dream had three parts. First, I died. Climbing the stairs was the death process. Second, I saw what death looked like in heaven, and how different it looked on earth. Third, I can't remember, but when I woke up I didn't know if I was dead or alive. I reached over to push the button on my husband's watch; it said 00:00. Naturally, I thought God was trying to tell me something. I thought I would die that day. I didn't know how or when, yet it was okay. I had seen the other side, and it was okay (that was another part of that dream). I saw how terrible death looked from earth and how wonderful it looked from heaven. I wanted to tell my family that I was going to die and that it was okay. As we traveled back to the Panhandle and were getting close to home, I was surprised that I was still alive. I looked down at my seven-year-old son asleep in my lap and I heard the Lord say, "I'm not finished with you yet." Of course, at the time, I didn't know that my son would be a doctor and help people get well physically and that I would help people get well spiritually. But God knew!

RECITING TODAY'S SCRIPTURE

Slowly, say out loud three times ...

Isaiah 53:4

Surely he hath borne our griefs, and carried our sorrows: yet we did esteem him stricken, smitten of God, and afflicted.

FILL IN THE BLANKS

1. Isaiah 53:4—_____ he _____ borne _____ griefs, _____ carried _____ sorrows: _____ we _____ esteem _____ stricken, _____ of _____, and _____.

2. _____—Surely _____ hath _____ our _____, and _____ our _____: yet _____ did _____ him _____, smitten _____ God, _____ afflicted.

3. Isaiah 53:4—Surely he hath borne our griefs, and carried our sorrows: _____.

4. Isaiah 53:4—_____: yet we did esteem him stricken, smitten of God, and afflicted.

5. _____—Surely he hath borne our griefs, and carried our sorrows: yet we did esteem him stricken, smitten of God, and afflicted.

6. Isaiah 53:4—_____

_____.

READ IT IN THE BIBLE

Find and read Isaiah 53:4 in your Bible.

WORD PUZZLE

Circle the hidden words in the puzzle below. Words may appear diagonally, vertically, horizontally, or backwards. Work puzzle in order as scripture is written here:

Surely he hath borne our griefs, and carried our sorrows: yet we did esteem him stricken, smitten of God, and afflicted.

```
A  S  M  I  T  T  E  N  D  A  A
F  N  K  W  N  H  I  M  O  S  D
F  O  D  A  E  T  L  S  G  U  I
L  Y  E  T  K  A  E  W  R  R  E
I  P  N  G  C  H  G  O  I  E  S
C  A  R  R  I  E  D  R  E  L  T
T  N  O  U  R  H  L  R  F  Y  E
E  D  B  O  T  I  I  O  S  E  E
D  I  D  O  S  M  B  S  S  T  M
```

SAY THE WORD SCRAMBLE

Recite today's scripture again. As you do, cross off each of the words as they appear in the list below.

sorrows yet borne Surely carried did Isaiah 53:4 he and esteem smitten hath griefs our stricken and our afflicted God we him of

PRAYING FROM GOD'S WORD

Pray for someone else right now, remembering that James 5:16 says, *"Pray one for another, that ye may be healed."*

YOUR THOUGHTS ON TODAY'S WORD

In the space below, write down what you have learned today as you meditate and dwell on our memory scripture.

_____
_____
_____
_____
_____
_____

EXTRA DAILY BIBLE READING

For an extra dose of God's Word, read Isaiah 53 and Roman 8:11.

HEALING MEDICINE

Read the Healing Medicine that appears at the end of this chapter now and at least twice more today.

NOTES

_____

_____

_____

_____

_____

_____

_____

_____

_____

_____

_____

❧

HIS COMPLETE WORK

Whatever you are suffering with today—whether it be physical, emotional, or mental suffering—Jesus took it upon Himself for you on the cross. The Word states that plainly. You say, "Then why am I suffering?" We have to appropriate that Word into our minds and spirit. We do this by planting seeds. Continue to get the Word into your spirit by working through this study. It's not the only way, but it is one way that has been designed just for you.

RECITING TODAY'S SCRIPTURE

Slowly, say out loud three times …

Isaiah 53:5

But he was wounded for our transgressions, he was bruised for our iniquities: the chastisement of our peace was upon him; and with his stripes we are healed.

FILL IN THE BLANKS

1. Isaiah 53:5—_____ he _____ wounded _____ our _____, he _____ bruised _____ our _____: the

_____ of _____ peace _____
upon _____; and _____ his _____
we _____ healed.

2. _____—But _____ was _____
for _____ transgressions, _____ was
_____ for _____ iniquities: _____
chastisement _____ our _____ was
_____ him; _____ with _____
stripes _____ are _____.

3. Isaiah 53:5—But he was wounded for our transgressions,
he was bruised for our iniquities: _____.

4. Isaiah 53:5—_____: the chastisement of our
peace was upon him; and with his stripes we are healed.

5. _____—But he was wounded for our transgressions, he was bruised for our iniquities: the chastisement of
our peace was upon him; and with his stripes we are healed.

6. Isaiah 53:5—_____

_____.

Read It In The Bible

Find and read Isaiah 53:5 in your Bible.

WORD PUZZLE

Circle the hidden words in the puzzle below. Words may
appear diagonally, vertically, horizontally, or backwards. Work
puzzle in order as scripture is written here:

70

But he was wounded for our transgressions, he was bruised for our iniquities: the chastisement of our peace was upon him; and with his stripes we are healed.

```
T  R  A  N  S  G  R  E  S  S  I  O  N  S  S
N  H  D  P  E  B  R  W  S  E  E  U  F  S  E
E  E  E  S  C  E  K  Q  U  R  R  R  O  L  I
M  L  N  W  A  S  J  S  G  A  A  S  R  D  T
E  R  U  O  E  W  I  T  H  N  N  E  A  N  I
S  T  R  I  P  E  S  M  L  L  L  P  W  A  U
I  S  R  F  U  U  R  I  F  C  C  I  E  G  Q
T  A  R  R  U  Q  B  H  I  S  S  R  H  E  I
S  W  O  U  N  D  E  D  E  M  M  T  T  P  N
A  E  F  O  R  S  L  M  A  K  K  S  U  K  I
H  E  A  L  E  D  E  S  I  U  R  B  B  S  D
C  S  A  L  L  Y  E  D  A  I  I  E  J  E  N
```

SAY THE WORD SCRAMBLE

Recite today's scripture again. As you do, cross off each of the words as they appear in the list below.

wounded stripes our with he bruised him we Isaiah 53:5 was he was was transgressions But peace healed for for iniquities are his of and the upon our our chastisement

71

PRAYING FROM GOD'S WORD

Pray this prayer out of God's Word, then wait on God to hear what He has to say to you. Use the space below to write what you hear.

Father, in Jesus' name, you say that if I call on you that you will answer and show me great and mighty things that I know not. I am calling on you for instruction from the Holy Spirit for my life and my healing. Give me your wisdom. Amen.

(Jeremiah 33:3; Philippians 2:10; Psalm 32:8)

_____

_____

_____

_____

YOUR THOUGHTS ON TODAY'S WORD

In the space below, write down what you have learned today as you meditate and dwell on our memory scripture.

_____

_____

_____

_____

EXTRA DAILY BIBLE READING

For an extra dose of God's Word, read Psalm 22.

HEALING MEDICINE

Read the Healing Medicine that appears at the end of this chapter now and at least twice more today.

NOTES

_____

_____

_____

_____

_____

_____

_____

_____

_____

_____

DAY 11

A MIGHTY WORK

We are still plating seeds! Planting seeds is what Jesus did on the cross. The blood and the cross have set you free from sin, sickness, and suffering. The blood of Jesus shows no favoritism. We probably never will be aware of all that the cross represented and what it did for us. We may never comprehend all that was in Jesus' heart and mind that day, yet there are some facts we do know, for instance:

It was the end of the Abrahamic Covenant. "*Neither by the blood of goats and calves, but by his own blood he entered in once into the holy place, having obtained eternal redemption for us*" (Hebrews 9:12). He was the ultimate sacrifice. No blood sacrifice would ever be needed again.

Some dead people were raised from their tombs and went into the city. "*And the graves were opened; and many bodies of the saints which slept* (were dead) *arose, and came out of the graves after his resurrection, and went into the holy city, and appeared unto many*" (Matthew 27:52-53).

On the cross, Jesus bore our sins and sicknesses. He was even chastised for our peace. Jesus has already done everything that he is going to do. So we must learn more about what he did and appropriate it into our being.

"*By his stripes we are healed*" Isaiah 53:5. We find examples of this in Matthew 27:26, Mark 15:15, and John 19:1. It also fulfills the prophesy found in Isaiah 53 and Psalm 22, and tells us that the prophecy was fulfilled in Matthew 8:17.

RECITING TODAY'S SCRIPTURE

Slowly, say out loud three times …

Matthew 8:17

That it might be fulfilled which was spoken by Esaias the prophet, saying, Himself took our infirmities, and bare our sicknesses.

FILL IN THE BLANKS

1. Matthew   8:17—_____   it   _____   be _____ which _____ spoken _____ Esaias _____ prophet, _____, Himself _____ our _____, and _____ our _____.

2. _____—That _____ might_____ fulfilled _____ was _____ by_____ the _____, saying, _____ took _____ infirmities, _____ bare _____ sicknesses.

3. Matthew 8:17—That it might be fulfilled which was spoken by Esaias the prophet, saying, _____.

4. Matthew 8:17—_____, Himself took our infirmities, and bare our sicknesses.

5. _____—That it might be fulfilled which was spoken by Esaias the prophet, saying, Himself took our infirmities, and bare our sicknesses.

6. Matthew 8:17—_____

_____.

READ IT IN THE BIBLE

Find and read Matthew 8:17 in your Bible.

WORD PUZZLE

Circle the hidden words in the puzzle below. Words may appear diagonally, vertically, horizontally, or backwards. Work puzzle in order as scripture is written here:

That it might be fulfilled which was spoken by Esaias the prophet, saying, Himself took our infirmities, and bare our sicknesses.

```
S  S  K  N  T  H  A  T  S  P  S  I
E  A  S  I  A  S  P  W  U  R  P  S
I  O  Y  S  R  L  J  D  O  O  R  E
T  O  R  I  B  U  T  N  Y  P  U  S
I  R  S  G  N  S  O  A  B  H  O  S
M  I  G  H  T  G  O  G  H  E  S  E
R  B  A  R  E  A  K  E  H  T  A  N
I  H  I  M  S  E  L  F  E  H  I  K
F  U  L  F  I  L  L  E  D  E  A  C
N  K  L  N  E  K  O  P  S  G  S  I
I  W  H  I  C  H  S  A  W  S  E  S
```

SAY THE WORD SCRAMBLE

Recite today's scripture again. As you do, cross off each of the words as they appear in the list below.

might fulfilled spoken bare sicknesses prophet the That be it saying Matthew 8:17 Esaias by which infirmities our Himself took was and our

PRAYING FROM GOD'S WORD

Write in your own words your prayer from God's Word.

_____

_____

_____

_____

_____

YOUR THOUGHTS ON TODAY'S WORD

In the space below, write down what you have learned today as you meditate and dwell on our memory scripture.

_____

_____

_____

_____

_____

EXTRA DAILY BIBLE READING

For an extra dose of God's Word, read Matthew 27:31–61 and Mark 15:20–47; 16:6.

HEALING MEDICINE

Read the Healing Medicine that appears at the end of this chapter now and at least twice more today.

NOTES

_____

_____

_____

_____

_____

_____

_____

_____

_____

LIVING UNTO RIGHTEOUSNESS

At one point in my life, I never liked reading about the cross. It always seemed like a sad story to me. Now, I look past the sadness and learn what was really happening. When Jesus said, *"It is finished,"* one of the things He was talking about was the Abrahamic Covenant. No longer was man bound by an animal sacrifice. The final scapegoat was sent out. Jesus became sin for us, and He was offered up for our sins. The man/God—the only man or deity that could pay that expensive price—was lifted up once and for all. Our sins were paid in full. Now, I look at the cross as the best thing that ever happened to me—and I hope you will, too.

RECITING TODAY'S SCRIPTURE

Slowly, say out loud three times ...

1 Peter 2:24

Who his own self bare our sins in his own body on the tree, that we, being dead to sins, should live unto righteousness: by whose stripes ye were healed.

FILL IN THE BLANKS

1. 1 Peter 2:24—_____ his _____ self

_____ our _____ in _____ own

_____ on _____ tree, _____ we,

_____ dead _____ sins, _____

live _____ righteousness: _____ whose

_____ ye _____ healed.

2. _____—Who _____ own _____

bare _____ sins _____ his _____

body _____ the _____, that

_____, being _____ to _____,

should _____ unto _____: by

_____ stripes _____ were _____.

3. 1 Peter 2:24—Who his own self bare our sins in his own
body on the tree, that we, being dead to sins,

_____.

4. 1 Peter 2:24—_____, should live unto righteousness: by whose stripes ye were healed.

5. _____—Who his own self bare our sins in his
own body on the tree, that we, being dead to sins, should
live unto righteousness: by whose stripes ye were healed.

6. 1 Peter 2:24—_____

_____.

READ IT IN THE BIBLE

Find and read 1 Peter 2:24 in your Bible.

WORD PUZZLE

Circle the hidden words in the puzzle below. Words may appear diagonally, vertically, horizontally, or backwards. Work puzzle in order as scripture is written here:

Who his own self bare our sins in his own body on the tree, that we, being dead to sins, should live unto righteousness: by whose stripes ye were healed.

```
J  L  E  R  E  W  S  T  R  I  P  E  S
S  S  E  N  S  U  O  E  T  H  G  I  R
E  I  R  U  Z  W  W  E  H  E  I  N  S
L  N  U  T  N  E  N  R  I  A  S  S  H
F  S  O  N  Y  T  A  T  S  L  E  I  O
W  D  E  A  D  Q  O  T  H  E  B  N  U
G  N  I  E  B  O  D  Y  S  D  N  S  L
S  E  V  I  L  E  S  O  H  W  P  B  D
T  A  H  T  B  L  X  Y  Y  B  A  R  E
P  Z  Y  X  L  O  T  N  U  D  A  B  C
```

SAY THE WORD SCRAMBLE

Recite today's scripture again. As you do, cross off each of the words as they appear in the list below.

self dead we sins Who should being his body live bare that our own own sins 1 Peter 2:24 in stripes tree, were whose unto his healed on by ye the to righteousness

PRAYING FROM GOD'S WORD

Pray this prayer from God's Word.

Father, in Jesus' name, I thank you that Jesus bore my sins on the tree (cross), that I am dead to sin, I live in righteousness, and by whose stripes I am healed. Amen.

(Philippians 2:10; 1 Peter 2:24)

YOUR THOUGHTS ON TODAY'S WORD

In the space below, write down what you have learned today as you meditate and dwell on our memory scripture.

_____

_____

_____

EXTRA DAILY BIBLE READING

For an extra dose of God's Word, read Luke 23:26–54; 24:6–7 and John 19:16–42; 20:11–17.

HEALING MEDICINE

Read the Healing Medicine that appears at the end of this chapter now and at least twice more today.

NOTES

_____

_____

_____

_____

༄

NO LONGER
UNDER A CURSE

"And when He had given thanks, he brake it, and said, Take, eat: this is my body, which is broken for you: this do in remembrance of me. After the same manner also he took the cup, when he had supped, saying, This cup is the new testament in my blood: this do ye as oft as ye drink it, in remembrance of me. For as often as ye eat this bread, and drink this cup, ye do shew the Lord's death till he come" (I Corinthians 11:24-26).

Communion is a wonderful experience. It is a procedure of partaking of the body and blood of our Lord Jesus Christ. I know that the terminology used is really frightening. It frightened me at first, too. Let me try to explain. Today, we "partake" of communion with crackers and grape juice. We use the Lord's Supper as our example. Many people are healed while taking communion. When we take it, we are appropriating what the cross did for us. We are also acting on what the Word says to do. Remember—we are still planting seeds when we put God's Word into motion!

RECITING TODAY'S SCRIPTURE

Slowly, say out loud three times ...

Galatians 3:13

Christ hath redeemed us from the curse of the law, being made a curse for us: for it is written, Cursed is every one that hangeth on a tree.

FILL IN THE BLANKS

1. Galatians 3:13—_____ hath _____ us _____ the _____ of _____ law, _____ made _____ curse _____ us: _____ it _____ written, _____ is _____ one _____ hangeth _____ _____.

2. _____—Christ _____ redeemed _____ from _____ curse _____ the _____, being _____ a _____ for _____: for _____ is _____, Cursed _____ every _____ that _____ on _____ tree.

3. Galatians 3:13—Christ hath redeemed us from the curse of the law, being made a curse for us: _____.

4. Galatians 3:13—_____: for it is written, Cursed is every one that hangeth on a tree.

5. _____—Christ hath redeemed us from the curse of the law, being made a curse for us: for it is written, Cursed is every one that hangeth on a tree.

6. Galatians 3:13—_____

_____.

READ IT IN THE BIBLE

Find and read Galatians 3:13 in your Bible.

WORD PUZZLE

Circle the hidden words in the puzzle below. Words may appear diagonally, vertically, horizontally, or backwards. Work puzzle in order as scripture is written here:

Christ hath redeemed us from the curse of the law, being made a curse for us: for it is written, Cursed is every one that hangeth on a tree.

```
R A T S I R H C A Y
F E F R O M A S L R
O O D E S R U C A E
R F N E T T I R W V
H A N G E T H A T E
E H T H E M A D E C
G N I E B I E D F U
T R E E S R U D O R
H R C U R S E D R S
E H A T H A T O N E
```

SAY THE WORD SCRAMBLE

Recite today's scripture again. As you do, cross off each of the words as they appear in the list below.

redeemed curse law Cursed every written it for curse us tree on hangeth that made being Christ Galatians 3:13 from hath the of one us the is a is for a

PRAYING FROM GOD'S WORD

Pray this prayer out of God's Word, then wait on God to hear what He has to say to you. Use the space below to write what you hear.

Father, in Jesus' name, you say that if I call on you that you will answer and show me great and mighty things that I know not. I am calling on you for instruction from the Holy Spirit for my life and my healing. Give me your wisdom. Amen.

(Jeremiah 33:3; Philippians 2:10; Psalm 32:8)

_____

_____

_____

_____

_____

_____

_____

_____

_____

_____

YOUR THOUGHTS ON TODAY'S WORD

In the space below, write down what you have learned today as you meditate and dwell on our memory scripture.

_____
_____
_____
_____
_____
_____

EXTRA DAILY BIBLE READING

For an extra dose of God's Word, read Deuteronomy 28 and Galatians 3.

HEALING MEDICINE

Read the Healing Medicine that appears at the end of this chapter now and at least twice more today.

NOTES

_____
_____
_____
_____
_____
_____
_____

UNDER HIS BLOOD

As I write to you about the cross, I feel a very strong spir-
itual attack against me. I know why. It is because the
cross and the blood are so important. As I was finishing this
book, I became very weak. It made me remember what it was
like before I was healed. I spent many years thinking about
and praying for others as this workbook came about. I was so
weak and tired that I hurt everywhere. Sometimes I could not
chew or swallow. That was probably one of the scariest things.
I want you to know that, just because I wrote this book, I'm not
immune to sickness. On the contrary, I know the benefits of
continuing to stand. I had to birth this book. Giving birth is not
always easy. My first child, Jennifer, weighed 7 pounds, 14
ounces. Giving birth to her was not too difficult. My son,
Craig, was 9 pounds, 14 1/2 ounces, and 23 inches long; that
was not easy! It was a long, hard birth, and I was very tiny. I
could not sit down for 12 days after he was born. He was
worth the price, and that is how I look at this workbook. This
book took a long time to birth out of my heart, spirit, and
mind. Even if only one person ever receives benefit from this
book, the work will have been worth it! We are all in this
together, this fight with Satan. We are joint heirs with Jesus
Christ, and *"greater is he that is within you than he that is in
the world"* (1 John 4:4).

RECITING TODAY'S SCRIPTURE

Slowly, say out loud three times ...

1 John 1:7

And the blood of Jesus Christ his Son cleanseth us from all sin.

FILL IN THE BLANKS

1. 1 John 1:7—_____ the _____ of
_____ Christ _____ Son _____ us
_____ all _____.

2. _____—And _____ blood
_____ Jesus _____ his _____
cleanseth _____ from _____ sin.

3. 1 John 1:7—And the blood of Jesus Christ his Son
_____.

4. 1 John 1:7—_____ cleanseth us from all sin.

5. _____—And the blood of Jesus Christ his Son
cleanseth us from all sin.

6. 1 John 1:7—_____
_____.

READ IT IN THE BIBLE

Find and read 1 John 1:7 in your Bible.

WORD PUZZLE

Circle the hidden words in the puzzle below. Words may appear diagonally, vertically, horizontally, or backwards. Work puzzle in order as scripture is written here:

And the blood of Jesus Christ his Son cleanseth us from all sin.

```
A N D J D O O L B F
L H I E A B F C S R
L I T S I N O O C O
D S H U E F G H N M
H T E S N A E L C I
N O S B T S I R H C
```

SAY THE WORD SCRAMBLE

Recite today's scripture again. As you do, cross off each of the words as they appear in the list below.

blood Jesus his cleanseth sin from and Christ the Son of 1 John 1:7 us all

PRAYING FROM GOD'S WORD

Pray this prayer out of God's Word.

Father, in Jesus' name, I thank you that your Son's blood cleanses me from all sin, and sickness. Amen.

(1 John 1:7)

YOUR THOUGHTS ON TODAY'S WORD

In the space below, write down what you have learned today as you meditate and dwell on our memory scripture.

_____

_____

_____

_____

EXTRA DAILY BIBLE READING

For an extra dose of God's Word, read Numbers 21:4–9, John 3:13–17, and John 12:32.

HEALING MEDICINE

Read the Healing Medicine that appears at the end of this chapter now and at least twice more today.

TEST TIME

Take the test located after this chapter's Healing Medicine.

NOTES

_____

_____

_____

_____

_____

_____

WEEK TWO HEALING MEDICINE

Psalms 107:20—*He sent his word, and healed them, and delivered them from their destructions.*

Isaiah 53:4—*Surely he hath borne our griefs, and carried our sorrows: yet we did esteem him stricken, smitten of God, and afflicted.*

Isaiah 53:5—*But he was wounded for our transgressions, he was bruised for our iniquities: the chastisement of our peace was upon him; and with his stripes we are healed.*

Matthew 8:17—*That it might be fulfilled which was spoken by Esaias the prophet, saying, Himself took our infirmities, and bare our sicknesses.*

1 Peter 2:24—*Who his own self bare our sins in his own body on the tree, that we, being dead to sins, should live unto righteousness: by whose stripes ye were healed.*

Galatians 3:13—*Christ hath redeemed us from the curse of the law, being made a curse for us: for it is written, Cursed is every one that hangeth on a tree.*

1 John 1:7—*And the blood of Jesus Christ his Son cleanseth us from all sin.*

WEEK TWO TEST

Fill In The Blanks

_____—*He sent his word, and healed them, and delivered them from their destructions.*

_____—*Surely he hath borne our griefs, and carried our sorrows: yet we did esteem him stricken, smitten of God, and afflicted.*

_____—*But he was wounded for our transgressions, he was bruised for our iniquities: the chastisement of our peace was upon him; and with his stripes we are healed.*

_____—*That it might be fulfilled which was spoken by Esaias the prophet, saying, Himself took our infirmities, and bare our sicknesses.*

_____—*Who his own self bare our sins in his own body on the tree, that we, being dead to sins, should live unto righteousness: by whose stripes ye were healed.*

_____—*Christ hath redeemed us from the curse of the law, being made a curse for us: for it is written, Cursed is every one that hangeth on a tree.*

_____—*And the blood of Jesus Christ his Son cleanseth us from all sin.*

Psalms 107:20—_____

Isaiah 53:4—_____

Isaiah 53:5—_____

Matthew 8:17—_____

1 Peter 2:24—_____

Galatians 3:13—_____

1 John 1:7—_____

Week Three

THE MIND AND MOUTH

STRONG IN HIM

When you feel weak, that is when you need to profess that you are strong. Words are powerful weapons, whether we use them for the good or the bad. Sometimes, when we are weak, it gives God a chance to be strong on our behalf. *"When the enemy comes in like a flood, the Spirit of the Lord raises up a standard against him"* (Isaiah 59:19). *"Be strong in the Lord..."* (Ephesians 6:10). You can do all things through Christ who strengthens you (Philippians 4:13). I want to speak strength over you today, in the name of Jesus. I say you are strong, according to Joel 3:10. Plant this word in your heart. You can do that by saying it. *"Let the weak say I am strong"* (Joel 3:10).

RECITING TODAY'S SCRIPTURE

Slowly, say out loud three times …

Joel 3:10

Let the weak say, I am strong.

FILL IN THE BLANKS

1. Joel 3:10—_____ the _____ say, _____ am _____.

2. _____—Let _____ weak _____,
I _____ strong.

3. Joel 3:10—Let the weak say, _____.

4. Joel 3:10—_____, I am strong.

5. _____—Let the weak say, I am strong.

6. Joel 3:10—_____.

READ IT IN THE BIBLE

Find and read Joel 3:10 in your Bible.

WORD PUZZLE

Circle the hidden words in the puzzle below. Words may appear diagonally, vertically, horizontally, or backwards. Work puzzle in order as scripture is written here:

Let the weak say, I am strong.

J L S T U W G

K O M A M N P

A S E C O R I

E P H R B E R

W Y T E L U I

H S A Y U L S

SAY THE WORD SCRAMBLE

Recite today's scripture again. As you do, cross off each of the words as they appear in the list below.

strong Joel 3:10 let weak I say the am

PRAYING FROM GOD'S WORD

Pray this prayer out of God's Word.

Father, in Jesus' name, I confess that I am strong, because your word says, *"Let the weak say, I am strong."* Amen.

(Philippians 2:10; Joel 3:10)

YOUR THOUGHTS ON TODAY'S WORD

In the space below, write down what you have learned today as you meditate and dwell on our memory scripture.

_____
_____
_____
_____
_____
_____

EXTRA DAILY BIBLE READING

For an extra dose of God's Word, read James 3:1–8.

HEALING MEDICINE

Read the Healing Medicine that appears at the end of this chapter now and at least twice more today.

NOTES

_____

_____

_____

_____

_____

_____

_____

_____

_____

DAY 16

STANDING TOGETHER

Are you suffering today? Remember—you are still planting seeds. When you call for the elders—leaders in the body of Christ—you will be planting good seeds. According to James 5:14, we should call for the elders of the church. James 5:15 says that if you have committed any sins they will be forgiven you. These are very important scriptures to stand on.

RECITING TODAY'S SCRIPTURE

Slowly, say out loud three times ...

James 5:14

Is any sick among you? let him call for the elders of the church; and let them pray over him, anointing him with oil in the name of the Lord.

FILL IN THE BLANKS

1. James 5:14—_____ any _____ among _____? let _____ call _____ the _____ of _____ church; _____ let _____ pray _____ him, _____

him _____ oil _____ the _____ of

_____ Lord.

2. _____—Is _____ sick _____

you? _____ him _____ for _____

elders _____ the _____; and

_____ them _____ over _____,

anointing _____ with _____ in

_____ name _____ the _____.

3. James 5:14—Is any sick among you? let him call for the
elders of the church _____.

4. James 5:14—_____, and let them pray over him,
anointing him with oil in the name of the Lord.

5. _____—Is any sick among you? let him call for
the elders of the church; and let them pray over him, anointing him with oil in the name of the Lord.

6. James 5:14—_____

_____.

READ IT IN THE BIBLE

Find and read James 5:14 in your Bible.

WORD PUZZLE

Circle the hidden words in the puzzle below. Words may
appear diagonally, vertically, horizontally, or backwards. Work
puzzle in order as scripture is written here:

Is any sick among you? let him call for the elders of the church; and let them pray over him, anointing him with oil in the name of the Lord.

G N I T N I O N A L

O T H E N A M E C O

F E S R E D L E H R

M H I M D L E T U D

A I C A L L T O R T

G M K M I H Y F C H

N W G L E A N O H E

O I N S I Y A R P D

M T R E V O N K S E

A H T H E U D L M F

SAY THE WORD SCRAMBLE

Recite today's scripture again. As you do, cross off each of the words as they appear in the list below.

sick let call elders him him them and name church Lord pray you? James 5:14 anointing for him Is oil the in of any among of over with let the the the

PRAYING FROM GOD'S WORD

Write in your own words your prayer from God's Word.

_____

_____

YOUR THOUGHTS ON TODAY'S WORD

In the space below, write down what you have learned today as you meditate and dwell on our memory scripture.

_____

_____

_____

_____

_____

EXTRA DAILY BIBLE READING

For an extra dose of God's Word, read James 5:13–18.

HEALING MEDICINE

Read the Healing Medicine that appears at the end of this chapter now and at least twice more today.

NOTES

_____

_____

_____

_____

_____

_____

_____

_____

_____

※

THOUGHT POWER

In order to plant the right seeds in your thoughts, you should only think positive thoughts. Then, your crop will grow up positive. Remember that you can't plant peas and get corn. Negative thoughts do not come from God! If you catch yourself having bad thoughts, replace that thought with scripture. For example: Every time you have a negative thought say 2 Corinthians 10:5 out loud (if possible). If need be, do it more than once. The devil will stop giving you negative thoughts because he doesn't want you to use scripture. So plant those good thoughts and let them grow!

RECITING TODAY'S SCRIPTURE

Slowly, say out loud three times ...

2 Corinthians 10:5

Casting down imaginations, and every high thing that exalteth itself against the knowledge of God, and bringing into captivity every thought to the obedience of Christ.

FILL IN THE BLANKS

1. 2 Corinthians 10:5—_____ down _____, and _____ high _____ that _____

itself _____ the _____ of _____,

and _____ into _____ every

_____ to _____ obedience _____

Christ.

2. _____—Casting _____ imaginations,

_____ every _____ thing _____

exalteth _____ against _____ knowledge

_____ God, _____ bringing _____

captivity _____ thought _____ the

_____ of _____.

3. 2 Corinthians 10:5—Casting down imaginations, and every high thing that exalteth itself against the knowledge of God, _____.

4. 2 Corinthians 10:5—_____, and bringing into captivity every thought to the obedience of Christ.

5. _____—Casting down imaginations, and every high thing that exalteth itself against the knowledge of God, and bringing into captivity every thought to the obedience of Christ.

6. 2 Corinthians 10:5—_____

_____.

READ IT IN THE BIBLE

Find and read 2 Corinthians 10:5 in your Bible.

WORD PUZZLE

Circle the hidden words in the puzzle below. Words may appear diagonally, vertically, horizontally, or backwards. Work puzzle in order as scripture is written here:

Casting down imaginations, and every high thing that exalteth itself against the knowledge of God, and bringing into captivity every thought to the obedience of Christ.

```
T  H  I  N  G  I  T  S  E  L  F  A
I  M  A  G  I  N  A  T  I  O  N  S
T  A  G  N  I  G  N  I  R  B  F  T
S  H  A  U  T  Y  R  E  V  E  O  H
E  A  I  G  O  S  S  T  H  D  O  A
L  O  N  N  D  Z  I  E  G  I  F  T
F  F  S  D  G  O  H  R  I  E  E  J
A  B  T  H  A  T  H  E  H  N  X  G
G  Y  T  I  V  I  T  P  A  C  A  N
A  O  H  H  T  O  Y  N  D  E  L  I
I  I  O  I  H  F  D  Z  O  V  T  T
N  N  U  J  E  O  N  W  W  E  E  S
S  T  G  S  T  U  A  V  N  R  T  A
T  O  H  T  S  I  R  H  C  Y  H  C
D  G  T  E  G  D  E  L  W  O  N  K
```

SAY THE WORD SCRAMBLE

Recite today's scripture again. As you do, cross off each of the words as they appear in the list below.

*obedience Casting captivity down and every high itself
against the knowledge of God and imaginations bringing into every thought to the that exalteth of Christ thing*

PRAYING FROM GOD'S WORD

Pray for someone else right now, remembering that James
5:16 says, *"Pray one for another, that ye may be healed."*

YOUR THOUGHTS ON TODAY'S WORD

In the space below, write down what you have learned
today as you meditate and dwell on our memory scripture.

EXTRA DAILY BIBLE READING

For an extra dose of God's Word, read Romans 8:1–11 and
1 Peter 3:1–15.

HEALING MEDICINE

Read the Healing Medicine that appears at the end of this
chapter now and at least twice more today.

NOTES

Day 17

FIRST RESPONSE

Just as we can choose our thoughts, we can choose our words. *"Out of the abundance of the heart the mouth speaketh"*(Luke 6:45). Let the Word that you have been planting in your heart speak to you. Line your mouth up with the Word of God. When trouble comes, the first words that come out of your mouth could and should be the word of God. God's words will work for you and not against you. Your first response—your first words—are the most important. They can win or lose the battle for you. We can also call things into being with our words. Abraham called things that were not as though they were. Speak the opposite of what the devil is telling you. Remember—he is a *"liar"* (John 8:44), and God's word is true. Here is a prayer example: *Lord, I am calling things that be not as though they were. I declare that I will walk in divine health, all my bills will be paid, I will have the strength to go to the doctor (or any other need you may have).* Prayer works! When you pray God's Word, you will always have results.

RECITING TODAY'S SCRIPTURE

Slowly, say out loud three times ...

Romans 4:17

And calleth those things which be not as though they were.

FILL IN THE BLANKS

1. Romans 4:17—_____ calleth _____
things _____ be _____ as _____
they _____.

2. _____—And _____ those
_____ which _____ not _____
though _____ were.

3. Romans 4:17—And calleth those things which be not
_____.

4. Romans 4:17—_____ as though they were.

5. _____—And calleth those things which be not as
though they were.

6. Romans 4:17—_____
_____.

READ IT IN THE BIBLE

Find and read Romans 4:17 in your Bible.

WORD PUZZLE

Circle the hidden words in the puzzle below. Words may
appear diagonally, vertically, horizontally, or backwards. Work
puzzle in order as scripture is written here:

*And calleth those things which be not as though they
were.*

SAY THE WORD SCRAMBLE

Recite today's scripture again. As you do, cross off each of the words as they appear in the list below.

they and those which not as calleth though were things be

PRAYING FROM GOD'S WORD

Pray this prayer out of God's Word, then wait on God to hear what He has to say to you. Use the space below to write what you hear.

Father, in Jesus' name, you say that if I call on you that you will answer and show me great and mighty things that I know not. I am calling on you for instruction from the Holy Spirit for my life and my healing. Give me your wisdom. Amen.

(Jeremiah 33:3; Philippians 2:10; Psalm 32:8)

YOUR THOUGHTS ON TODAY'S WORD

In the space below, write down what you have learned today as you meditate and dwell on our memory scripture.

_____

_____

_____

_____

_____

EXTRA DAILY BIBLE READING

For an extra dose of God's Word, read Matthew 6:25-34 and Mark 11:25.

HEALING MEDICINE

Read the Healing Medicine that appears at the end of this chapter now and at least twice more today.

NOTES

_____

_____

_____

_____

_____

_____

_____

_____

_____

BIND IT OR LOOSE IT

Binding and loosing is another way of planting seeds. Binding and loosing can be intentional or unintentional. For example: You could bind up someone's healing or even your own by un-forgiveness, speaking negative words, or even disobedience. We can also bless people, which is a form of loosing. This can be done by forgiveness or speaking blessings, praying for each other, or even being obedient. I realize these are only a couple of examples. Much power is tied up in the idea binding and loosing, and I would need a lot more time and space to speak further on the subject! Pray and ask God to show you more about binding and loosing.

RECITING TODAY'S SCRIPTURE

Slowly, say out loud three times ...

Matthew 18:18

Whatsoever ye shall bind on earth shall be bound in heaven: and whatsoever ye shall loose on earth shall be loosed in heaven.

Day 19

FILL IN THE BLANKS

1. Matthew 18:18—_____ ye _____ bind

_____ earth _____ be _____ in

_____: and _____ ye _____ loose

_____ earth _____ be _____ in

_____.

2. _____—Whatsoever _____ shall

_____ on _____ shall _____

bound _____ heaven: _____ whatsoever

_____ shall _____ on _____ shall

_____ loosed _____ heaven.

3. Matthew 18:18—Whatsoever ye shall bind on earth shall
be bound in heaven: _____.

4. Matthew 18:18—_____: and whatsoever ye shall
loose on earth shall be loosed in heaven.

5. _____—Whatsoever ye shall bind on earth shall
be bound in heaven: and whatsoever ye shall loose on earth
shall be loosed in heaven.

6. Matthew 18:18—_____

_____.

READ IT IN THE BIBLE

Find and read Matthew 18:18 in your Bible.

113

WORD PUZZLE

Circle the hidden words in the puzzle below. Words may appear diagonally, vertically, horizontally, or backwards. Work puzzle in order as scripture is written here:

Whatsoever ye shall bind on earth shall be bound in heaven: and whatsoever ye shall loose on earth shall be loosed in heaven.

```
R  E  V  E  O  S  T  A  H  W
Q  Y  W  D  N  I  B  E  D  H
R  V  E  E  I  A  E  I  J  A
S  N  A  S  X  Y  E  G  H  T
T  E  R  O  Y  Z  N  D  E  S
L  V  T  O  L  O  O  S  E  O
L  A  H  L  B  O  U  N  D  E
A  E  A  R  T  H  C  D  M  V
H  H  E  A  V  E  N  L  N  E
S  H  A  L  L  A  H  S  O  R
I  N  Y  E  N  E  V  A  E  H
```

SAY THE WORD SCRAMBLE

Recite today's scripture again. As you do, cross off each of the words as they appear in the list below.

whatsoever ye shall bind on earth shall be bound in heaven and whatsoever ye shall loose on earth shall be loosed in heaven

PRAYING FROM GOD'S WORD

Pray this prayer out of God's Word.

Father, in Jesus' name, your word says that whatever I bind on earth is bound in heaven, and whatever I loose on earth is loosed in heaven. Therefore, I bind sickness and disease from my body, and loose health and healing upon my body, in Jesus' name. Amen. (Philippians 2:10; Matthew 18:18)

YOUR THOUGHTS ON TODAY'S WORD

In the space below, write down what you have learned today as you meditate and dwell on our memory scripture.

_____

_____

EXTRA DAILY BIBLE READING

For an extra dose of God's Word, read Philippians 4:4–13, 19.

HEALING MEDICINE

Read the Healing Medicine that appears at the end of this chapter now and at least twice more today.

NOTES

_____

_____

_____

DAY 20

꧁꧂

LOCKING ARMS

One of my favorite scriptures that I put into practice is
Matthew 18:19. Agreeing in prayer with someone is very
important. I personally don't understand why we don't obey
when God makes a thing so clear, such as his word. *"Again I
say to you, That if two of you shall agree on earth as touching
anything that they shall ask, it shall be done for them of my
Father which is in heaven."* (Matthew 18:19) I have many stories that I could tell about agreeing. The one that comes to
mind is the one about my namesake. We have a pond in our
backyard. It has a fountain, aquatic plants, and three large
willows draping over it, shading the pond. We spend quite a
lot of time out there. We have several different kinds of gold-
fish. We have one that is white, a little overweight, and has a
red head. We call her Peggy Ann after you know who. One day
Craig, my son said he was a little worried about Peggy Ann. I
hadn't noticed anything. He took me over to the pond and
there she was on her side heaving. Craig asked if I would
agree with him that Peggy Ann would be okay. I agreed, even
though, in my mind, I was thinking how bad this looked. At
the time I noticed how fat she looked. My granddaughter and
I went back a little later to see if there had been any change.
She made the remark that Peggy Ann looked fat. By now she
was floating upside down and things looked pretty hopeless.
Craig said that he had never saved a fish that was this bad.

116

That didn't help my faith any; we agreed in prayer anyway. I told Craig that she looked extra fat and that maybe she was plugged up. I suggested that he squeeze her tummy just a little and see what happens. When he squeezed her, air bubbles came out. Then she went to the bottom and has been fine ever since. God is so good! Even the little things matter to God. Agreeing in prayer with someone really works.

RECITING TODAY'S SCRIPTURE

Slowly, say out loud three times ...

Matthew 18:19

That if two of you shall agree on earth as touching any thing that they shall ask, it shall be done for them of my Father which is in heaven.

FILL IN THE BLANKS

1. Matthew 18:19—_____ if _____ of
_____ shall _____ on _____ as
_____ any _____ that _____ shall
_____ , it _____ be _____ for
_____ of _____ Father _____ is
_____ heaven.

2. _____— That __ two __ you ___ agree __ earth
__ touching ___ thing ___ they _____ ask, __ shall __ done
___ them __ my _____ which __ in _____.

3. Matthew 18:19— That if two of you shall agree on earth as touching any thing that they shall ask, _____.

4. Matthew 18:19—_____, it shall be done for them of my Father which is in heaven.

5. _____—That if two of you shall agree on earth as touching any thing that they shall ask, it shall be done for them of my Father which is in heaven.

6. Matthew 18:19—_____

_____.

READ IT IN THE BIBLE

Find and read Matthew 18:19 in your Bible.

WORD PUZZLE

Circle the hidden words in the puzzle below. Words may appear diagonally, vertically, horizontally, or backwards. Work puzzle in order as scripture is written here:

That if two of you shall agree on earth as touching any thing that they shall ask, it shall be done for them of my Father which is in heaven.

```
G  N  I  H  C  U  O  T  T  F  O  S
L  E  F  O  O  F  W  H  H  A  S  U
L  N  F  G  U  O  Y  A  E  T  I  H
A  O  E  N  H  R  I  T  M  H  N  C
H  D  D  I  G  I  B  E  L  E  E  I
S  Y  E  H  T  R  A  E  L  R  V  H
T  A  H  T  C  Y  J  R  A  K  A  W
H  E  S  A  B  M  N  G  H  L  E  L
S  H  A  L  L  K  S  A  S  M  H  P
```

SAY THE WORD SCRAMBLE

Recite today's scripture again. As you do, cross off each of the words as they appear in the list below.

two you agree as done Matthew 18:19 That heaven. ask, shall they shall Father which of if shall is earth for them be on of touching any thing that my in it

PRAYING FROM GOD'S WORD

Pray this prayer out of God's Word.

Father, in Jesus' name, your word says that if I agree with someone on earth that it will be done in heaven. (Find someone to agree with you for health and healing in your body.) Thank you Father for your word. Amen.

(Philippians 2:10; Matthew 18:19)

YOUR THOUGHTS ON TODAY'S WORD

In the space below, write down what you have learned today as you meditate and dwell on our memory scripture.

_____

_____

_____

_____

EXTRA DAILY BIBLE READING

For an extra dose of God's Word, read Isaiah 55:6–13.

HEALING MEDICINE

Read the Healing Medicine that appears at the end of this chapter now and at least twice more today.

NOTES

_____

_____

_____

_____

_____

_____

_____

_____

_____

_____

CONFESS— AND BELIEVE!

By planting this next seed and acting on Romans 10:9, you can have God's salvation. You can also have eternal life. All you have to do is ask and truly believe. The verse says that if you confess with your mouth the Lord Jesus and believe in your heart that God raised him from the dead, then you will be saved. The word "saved" also means to be healed. So, the same scripture can heal you in the midst of your suffering. God's Word has so many answers to so many problems. If you read His Word, He will show you what is applicable to you and what specific word to stand on.

RECITING TODAY'S SCRIPTURE

Slowly, say out loud three times ...

Romans 10:9

That if thou shall confess with thy mouth the Lord Jesus, and shalt believe in thine heart that God hath raised him from the dead, thou shalt be saved.

121

FILL IN THE BLANKS

1. Romans 10:9—____ if ____ shall _____ with __ mouth __ Lord _____, and ____ believe __ thine _____ that ___ hath _____ him ___ the ____, thou ____ be ____.

2. _____— That __ thou _____ confess ____ thy _____ the ____ Jesus, ___ shalt _____ in ____ heart ____ God ____ raised ___ from __ dead, ____ shalt __ saved.

3. Romans 10:9—That if thou shall confess with thy mouth the Lord Jesus, _____.

4. Romans 10:9—_____, and shalt believe in thine heart that God hath raised him from the dead, thou shalt be saved.

5. _____—That if thou shall confess with thy mouth the Lord Jesus, and shalt believe in thine heart that God hath raised him from the dead, thou shalt be saved.

6. Romans 10:9—_____

_____.

READ IT IN THE BIBLE

Find and read Romans 10:9 in your Bible.

WORD PUZZLE

Circle the hidden words in the puzzle below. Words may appear diagonally, vertically, horizontally, or backwards. Work puzzle in order as scripture is written here:

That if thou shall confess with thy mouth the Lord Jesus, and shalt believe in thine heart that God hath raised him from the dead, thou shalt be saved.

```
T   H   O   U   A   G   H   C   E

H   E   A   R   T   O   T   O   V

O   T   H   A   T   D   U   N   E

U   T   H   I   N   E   O   F   I

J   E   S   U   S   H   M   E   L

T   H   E   H   T   T   A   S   E

L   F   A   L   O   R   D   S   B

A   T   A   I   D   E   A   D   D

H   H   C   N   Y   H   T   I   W

S   H   A   L   L   T   H   A   T
```

SAY THE WORD SCRAMBLE

Recite today's scripture again. As you do, cross off each of the words as they appear in the list below.

thou shalt saved hath shalt God confess thy mouth the Jesus Lord raised him heart with That dead from the that believe thine in shall Romans 10:9 if and be thou

PRAYING FROM GOD'S WORD

Pray this prayer out of God's Word.

Father, in Jesus' name, forgive me of my sins. I believe that Jesus is Lord, and that you raised him from the dead. I believe that I am saved by the blood of Jesus Christ. Thank you for giving your son so that I could be saved. Amen.

(Philippians 2:10; Romans 10:9)

[Tell someone that you are saved—or healed. (Romans 10:10)]

YOUR THOUGHTS ON TODAY'S WORD

In the space below, write down what you have learned today as you meditate and dwell on our memory scripture.

_____

_____

_____

_____

EXTRA DAILY BIBLE READING

For an extra dose of God's Word, read Romans 10:1–13.

HEALING MEDICINE

Read the Healing Medicine that appears at the end of this chapter now and at least twice more today.

TEST TIME

Take the test located after this chapter's Healing Medicine.

NOTES

_____

_____

_____

_____

_____

_____

_____

_____

_____

_____

WEEK THREE HEALING MEDICINE

Joel 3:10—*Let the weak say, I am strong.*

James 5:14—*Is any sick among you? let him call for the elders of the church; and let them pray over him, anointing him with oil in the name of the Lord.*

2 Corinthians 10:5—*Casting down imaginations, and every high thing that exalteth itself against the knowledge of God, and bringing into captivity every thought to the obedience of Christ.*

Romans 4:17—*And calleth those things which be not as though they were.*

Matthew 18:18—*Whatsoever ye shall bind on earth shall be bound in heaven: and whatsoever ye shall loose on earth shall be loosed in heaven.*

Matthew 18:19—*That if two of you shall agree on earth as touching any thing that they shall ask, it shall be done for them of my Father which is in heaven.*

Romans 10:9—*That if thou shall confess with thy mouth the Lord Jesus, and shalt believe in thine heart that God hath raised him from the dead, thou shalt be saved.*

WEEK THREE TEST

Fill In The Blanks

_____—*Let the weak say, I am strong.*

_____—*Is any sick among you? let him call for the elders of the church; and let them pray over him, anointing him with oil in the name of the Lord.*

_____—*Casting down imaginations, and every high thing that exalteth itself against the knowledge of God, and bringing into captivity every thought to the obedience of Christ.*

_____—*And calleth those things which be not as though they were.*

_____—*Whatsoever ye shall bind on earth shall be bound in heaven: and whatsoever ye shall loose on earth shall be loosed in heaven.*

126

_____—*That if two of you shall agree on earth as touching any thing that they shall ask, it shall be done for them of my Father which is in heaven.*

_____—*That if thou shalt confess with thy mouth the Lord Jesus, and shalt believe in thine heart that God hath raised him from the dead, thou shalt be saved.*

Joel 3:10—_____

_____

James 5:14—_____

_____

II Corinthians 10:5—_____

_____

Romans 4:17—_____

_____

Matthew 18:18—_____

_____

Matthew 18:19—_____

_____

Romans 10:9—_____

_____

Week Four

FAITH AND FEAR

REPLACING FEAR WITH FAITH

Did you know that your righteousness has nothing to do with what you have done in your life? It has only to do with what Jesus did on the cross. When you believe that Jesus was raised from the grave and confess the same with your mouth, only then are you righteous. You begin to see things in a different light—and faith replaces fear in your life. You realize the importance of the blood that was shed, the life that was freely given, and the stripes that He bore.

RECITING TODAY'S SCRIPTURE

Slowly, say out loud three times ...

Romans 10:10

For with the heart man believeth unto righteousness; and with the mouth confession is made unto salvation.

FILL IN THE BLANKS

1. Romans 10:10—____ with ___ heart ___ believeth ____

righteousness; ___ with ___ mouth _____ is ___ unto

_____.

2. _____—For ____ the _____ man _____ unto
_____; and ____ the _____ confession __ made ___
salvation.

3. Romans 10:10— For with the heart man believeth unto
righteousness; _____.

4. Romans 10:10—_____; and with the mouth confession is made unto salvation.

5. _____—For with the heart man believeth unto
righteousness; and with the mouth confession is made unto
salvation.

6. Romans 10:10—_____

_____.

READ IT IN THE BIBLE

Find and read Romans 10:10 in your Bible.

WORD PUZZLE

Circle the hidden words in the puzzle below. Words may
appear diagonally, vertically, horizontally, or backwards. Work
puzzle in order as scripture is written here:

*For with the heart man believeth unto righteousness;
and with the mouth confession is made unto salvation.*

```
A  N  O  I  T  A  V  L  A  S  J  T  A
B  A  G  A  H  N  U  A  C  C  K  H  C
C  M  H  B  E  D  V  E  D  O  L  E  E
D  O  I  E  H  N  D  B  E  N  M  W  G
H  U  J  L  T  A  W  R  O  F  N  I  I
T  T  K  I  M  R  X  T  F  E  O  T  J
I  H  L  E  O  S  N  T  G  S  P  H  L
W  B  M  V  P  U  R  O  H  S  Q  A  M
E  I  N  E  Q  A  Y  T  S  I  R  B  O
F  A  X  T  E  T  Z  N  I  O  S  C  Q
R  I  G  H  T  E  O  U  S  N  E  S  S
```

SAY THE WORD SCRAMBLE

Recite today's scripture again. As you do, cross off each of the words as they appear in the list below.

heart man righteousness For the with unto Romans 10:10 salvation mouth and believeth with the confession made is unto

PRAYING FROM GOD'S WORD

Pray this prayer out of God's Word.

Father, in Jesus' name, I believe I am righteous through the blood of Jesus, and I confess with my mouth that I am saved, and that Jesus is Lord of my Life. Amen.

(Philippians 2:10; Romans 10:10)

YOUR THOUGHTS ON TODAY'S WORD

In the space below, write down what you have learned today as you meditate and dwell on our memory scripture.

_____

EXTRA DAILY BIBLE READING

For an extra dose of God's Word, read Acts 9:1–34,19:11–12.

HEALING MEDICINE

Read the Healing Medicine that appears at the end of this chapter now and at least twice more today.

NOTES

_____

DAY 23

⁂

SPEAK IT!

Here is another powerful seed to plant in your heart. Say the Word with your mouth and believe the Word with you heart. God's words are very powerful, more than we can ever imagine. In Genesis 1, God formed the earth and all that is in it with His words. Jesus said, according to John 14:12, that we can do even greater works than He did when He walked the earth—if you believe in Him. Plant this scripture by using this example: "Suffering, I command you to be gone! I believe in my heart that suffering is gone in Jesus' name." When we speak out loud, it adds faith to our prayers—and displaces the fear in our hearts. I encourage you to speak the Word!

RECITING TODAY'S SCRIPTURE

Slowly, say out loud three times ...

Mark 11:23

That whosoever shall say unto this mountain, Be thou removed, and be thou cast into the sea; and shall not doubt in his heart, but shall believe that those things which he saith shall come to pass; he shall have whatsoever he saith.

133

WHY SIT HERE TILL WE DIE

FILL IN THE BLANKS

1. Mark 11:23—____ whosoever _____ say ____ this
_____, Be ____ removed, ___ be ____ cast ____ the ___;
and _____ not _____ in ___ heart, ___ shall _____ that _____
things _____ he _____ shall ____ to ____; he _____ have
_____ he _____.

2. _____—That _____ shall ___ unto ____
mountain, __ thou _____, and __ thou ____ into ___
sea; ___ shall ___ doubt __ his _____, but _____ believe ____
those _____ which __ saith _____ come __ pass; __
shall ____ whatsoever __ saith.

3. Mark 11:23—That whosoever shall say unto this mountain, Be thou removed, and be thou cast into the sea; and
shall not doubt in his heart, _____.

4. Mark 11:23—_____; but shall believe that those
things which he saith shall come to pass; he shall have
whatsoever he saith.

5. _____—That whosoever shall say unto this mountain, Be thou removed, and be thou cast into the sea; and shall
not doubt in his heart, but shall believe that those things which
he saith shall come to pass; he shall have whatsoever he saith.

6. Mark 11:23—_____
_____.

READ IT IN THE BIBLE

Find and read Mark 11:23 in your Bible.

WORD PUZZLE

Circle the hidden words in the puzzle below. Words may appear diagonally, vertically, horizontally, or backwards. Work puzzle in order as scripture is written here:

That whosoever shall say unto this mountain, Be thou removed, and be thou cast into the sea; and shall not doubt in his heart, but shall believe that those things which he saith shall come to pass; he shall have whatsoever he saith.

```
S W H A T S O E V E R B T O S E
H H H E H A N D E C E E H P H V
A A E S A Y O U R O M L I L A A
L T S H A L L N I M O I N L L H
L S H A L L I T L E V E G A L R
T O N I N T O O Y B E V S H Q S
H E C T S A C J B B D E M S A H
O V H D T D O U B T K S S A P T
U E D N A F T S H A L L N I F I
T R A E H G N O T H O S E T O A
B N I A T N U O M W H I C H R S
W H O S O E V E R V A H T A H T
```

SAY THE WORD SCRAMBLE

Recite today's scripture again. As you do, cross off each of the words as they appear in the list below.

his in into to thou the this Be but whosoever thou cast doubt have unto removed Mark 11:23 heart believe shall shall say whatsoever saith saith That mountain pass and sea shall shall shall be things that come and not those which he he he

PRAYING FROM GOD'S WORD

Pray this prayer out of God's Word.

Father, in Jesus' name, your word says that whatever I say that I can have as long as I believe it in my heart. Therefore, I say, "Suffering, be removed from my life." I believe in my heart that I am whole, in Jesus' name. Amen.

(Mark 11:23)

YOUR THOUGHTS ON TODAY'S WORD

In the space below, write down what you have learned today as you meditate and dwell on our memory scripture.

_____

_____

_____

_____

_____

EXTRA DAILY BIBLE READING

For an extra dose of God's Word, read John 11:1–44 and Acts 20:7–12.

HEALING MEDICINE

Read the Healing Medicine that appears at the end of this chapter now and at least twice more today.

NOTES

_____

_____

_____

_____

_____

_____

_____

_____

_____

✿

GODLY DESIRES

Another "say and believe" formula that has been very effective in my life is desire-pray-believe-receive. God gives us desires. I'm not talking about wishing for a new car or a sum of money. I'm not talking about "naming it and claiming it." I'm talking about God giving us right desires in our hearts—and then our praying and believing that we shall receive. God meets our needs according to his riches in glory by Christ Jesus (Philippians 4:19). God wants us to be blessed. We simply need to have our desires line up with the Word of God. Continue to plant seeds of God's Word and you will have a harvest in due season. Remember the law of seedtime and harvest, so plant in faith, not fear, and you will reap a harvest of faith!

RECITING TODAY'S SCRIPTURE

Slowly, say out loud three times ...

Mark 11:24

Therefore I say unto you, What things soever ye desire, when ye pray, believe that ye receive them, and ye shall have them.

FILL IN THE BLANKS

1. Mark 11:24—_____ I __ unto ___, What _____ soever __ desire, ____ ye ____, believe ____ ye _____ them, ___ ye _____ have ____.

2. _____—Therefore _ say ____ you, ____ things _____ ye _____, when __ pray, _____ that __ receive ____, and __ shall ____ them.

3. Mark 11:24—Therefore I say unto you, What things soever ye desire, when ye pray, _____.

4. Mark 11:24—_____, believe that ye receive them, and ye shall have them.

5. _____—Therefore I say unto you, What things soever ye desire, when ye pray, believe that ye receive them, and ye shall have them.

6. Mark 11:24—_____

_____.

READ IT IN THE BIBLE

Find and read Mark 11:24 in your Bible.

WORD PUZZLE

Circle the hidden words in the puzzle below. Words may appear diagonally, vertically, horizontally, or backwards. Work puzzle in order as scripture is written here:

Therefore I say unto you, What things soever ye desire, when ye pray, believe that ye receive them, and ye shall have them.

```
T  H  E  R  E  F  O  R  E  T  H
H  W  V  E  Y  E  Y  E  F  H  A
I  H  E  V  S  H  A  L  L  E  V
N  E  I  E  R  I  S  E  D  M  E
G  N  L  O  T  N  U  O  Y  H  T
S  E  E  S  A  Y  A  R  P  I  H
B  C  B  E  L  I  E  V  E  J  E
R  E  C  E  I  V  E  A  N  D  M
T  H  A  T  W  H  A  T  G  K  L
```

SAY THE WORD SCRAMBLE

Recite today's scripture again. As you do, cross off each of the words as they appear in the list below.

ye ye ye ye that believe shall receive Mark 11:24 Therefore desire What soever I say pray them and when you have things unto them

PRAYING FROM GOD'S WORD

Pray for someone else right now, remembering that James 5:16 says, *"Pray one for another, that ye may be healed."*

YOUR THOUGHTS ON TODAY'S WORD

In the space below, write down what you have learned today as you meditate and dwell on our memory scripture.

_____

_____

_____
_____
_____

EXTRA DAILY BIBLE READING

For an extra dose of God's Word, read Hebrews 11 and Acts 19:11–12.

HEALING MEDICINE

Read the Healing Medicine that appears at the end of this chapter now and at least twice more today.

NOTES

_____
_____
_____
_____
_____
_____
_____
_____
_____
_____

DAY 25

❧❧❧

FIGHTING FEAR

Fear is not from God. Fear is one of the devil's greatest weapons against us. Fear can paralyze you—and even make you sick. We continue to hear about stress-related illnesses. I think that fear was the root cause of my own illness. Now, though, God has helped me overcome my fears. As a child, I was afraid of everything, especially snakes. I can actually hold them now! When fear comes upon you like a thief in the night, you need to have these scriptures about fear planted in your heart. Use them as weapons against fear. Angels hearken to God's words, as do demons and Satan. It is the best defense you have in this world. How is your garden today? Do you have seeds sprouting?

RECITING TODAY'S SCRIPTURE

Slowly, say out loud three times ...

Isaiah 41:10

Fear thou not; for I am with thee: be not dismayed; for I am thy God: I will strengthen thee; yea, I will help thee; yea, I will uphold thee with the right hand of my righteousness.

FILL IN THE BLANKS

1. Isaiah 41:10—____ thou ___; for _ am ____ thee: __ not
_____; for _ am ___ God: _ will _____ thee; ___, I
____ help ___; yea, _ will _____ thee ____ the _____
hand __ my _____.

2. _____—Fear ____ not; ___ I _ with ___: be __
dismayed; ___ I _ thy ___: I ____ strengthen ___; yea, _ will
____ thee; ___, I ____ uphold ___ with ___ right ____ of _
righteousness.

3. Isaiah 41:10—Fear thou not; for I am with thee: be not
dismayed; for I am thy God: I will strengthen thee;

_____.

4. Isaiah 41:10—_____; yea, I will help thee; yea, I
will uphold thee with the right hand of my righteousness.

5. _____— Fear thou not; for I am with thee: be not
dismayed; for I am thy God: I will strengthen thee; yea, I will
help thee; yea, I will uphold thee with the right hand of my
righteousness.

6. Isaiah 41:10—_____

_____.

READ IT IN THE BIBLE

Find and read Isaiah 41:10 in your Bible.

WORD PUZZLE

Circle the hidden words in the puzzle below. Words may appear diagonally, vertically, horizontally, or backwards. Work puzzle in order as scripture is written here:

Fear thou not; for I am with thee: be not dismayed; for I am thy God: I will strengthen thee; yea, I will help thee; yea, I will uphold thee with the right hand of my righteousness.

```
D  I  S  M  A  Y  E  D  N  O  T  H  U
A  D  N  A  H  E  B  W  I  L  L  E  P
T  H  E  E  F  A  E  L  W  I  L  L  H
R  T  H  E  E  G  I  U  O  H  T  P  O
O  A  C  Y  T  W  I  T  H  F  H  I  L
F  O  R  E  H  I  Y  H  T  D  G  J  D
E  T  H  E  E  T  M  F  O  W  I  L  L
A  B  D  N  E  H  T  G  N  E  R  T  S
R  I  G  H  T  E  O  U  S  N  E  S  S
```

SAY THE WORD SCRAMBLE

Recite today's scripture again. As you do, cross off each of the words as they appear in the list below.

strengthen uphold dismayed help right for I am thy God I will thee yea I will thee yea I will thee with the hand of my righteousness Isaiah 41:10 Fear not for I am with thee be not thou

144

PRAYING FROM GOD'S WORD

Write in your own words your prayer from God's Word.

_____

_____

_____

YOUR THOUGHTS ON TODAY'S WORD

In the space below, write down what you have learned today as you meditate and dwell on our memory scripture.

_____

_____

_____

EXTRA DAILY BIBLE READING

For an extra dose of God's Word, read 1 Corinthians 13 and 1 John 4:18.

HEALING MEDICINE

Read the Healing Medicine that appears at the end of this chapter now and at least twice more today.

NOTES

_____

_____

_____

_____

POWER FROM ON HIGH

God has given us a spirit of power, love, and a sound mind (2 Timothy 1:17). Fear is from Satan. Perfect love casts out fear (1 John 4:18). I've been trying to learn about perfect love. I know that God's love is perfect—the only perfect love. I believe that, if we walk in love, we will have less fear. We will have power, while, on the other hand, fear can make us powerless. When you are fearful, plant the Word. Talk to the fear; demand that it leave in the name of Jesus. God's Word says that he has given us a spirit of power, love, and a sound mind. Plant this word and get a harvest of faith to live with power, love, and a sound mind.

RECITING TODAY'S SCRIPTURE

Slowly, say out loud three times ...

2 Timothy 1:7

For God hath not given us the spirit of fear; but of power, and of love, and of a sound mind.

Day 26

FILL IN THE BLANKS

1. 2 Timothy 1:7—___ God ____ not _____ us ___ spirit __ fear; ___ of ____, and __ love, ___ of _ sound ____.

2. _____—For ___ hath ___ given __ the _____ of ____; but _ power, ___ of ____, and __ a ____ mind.

3. 2 Timothy 1:7—For God hath not given us the spirit of fear; _____.

4. 2 Timothy 1:7—_____; yea but of power, and of love, and of a sound mind.

5. _____—For God hath not given us the spirit of fear; but of power, and of love, and of a sound mind.

6. 2 Timothy 1:7—_____

_____.

READ IT IN THE BIBLE

Find and read 2 Timothy 1:7 in your Bible.

WORD PUZZLE

Circle the hidden words in the puzzle below. Words may appear diagonally, vertically, horizontally, or backwards. Work puzzle in order as scripture is written here:

For God hath not given us the spirit of fear; but of power, and of love, and of a sound mind.

147

S O U N D P M A G A

P F S O O O I R I N

I E H T G W N A V D

R A N D A E D E E B

I O F F B R O F N U

T L O V E H A T H T

SAY THE WORD SCRAMBLE

Recite today's scripture again. As you do, cross off each of the words as they appear in the list below.

power, and of and of a sound 2 Timothy 1:7 For God given us fear of mind love hath spirit but not of the

PRAYING FROM GOD'S WORD

Pray this prayer out of God's Word, then wait on God to hear what He has to say to you. Use the space below to write what you hear.

Father, in Jesus' name, you say that if I call on you that you will answer and show me great and mighty things that I know not. I am calling on you for instruction from the Holy Spirit for my life and my healing. Give me your wisdom. Amen.

(Jeremiah 33:3; Philippians 2:10; Psalm 32:8)

YOUR THOUGHTS ON TODAY'S WORD

In the space below, write down what you have learned today as you meditate and dwell on our memory scripture.

_____
_____
_____
_____
_____

EXTRA DAILY BIBLE READING

For an extra dose of God's Word, read Job 1, 19, 42.

HEALING MEDICINE

Read the Healing Medicine that appears at the end of this chapter now and at least twice more today.

NOTES

_____
_____
_____
_____
_____
_____
_____
_____
_____

PLANT YOUR SEEDS IN FAITH

L ong ago, I would tell people that God was going to heal me and that He could heal them also. I could not tell them where it said that in the Bible, so my words seemed empty (to me, anyway). I may have had a garden, yet there were no seeds planted there. You cannot have a garden and expect it to grow without seeds. All you will grow are weeds—and you can't live off of weeds. Don't make the mistake I did. Get those seeds of faith planted. Live in obedience to God. Walk in love and receive a harvest of God's healing power.

RECITING TODAY'S SCRIPTURE

Slowly, say out loud three times ...

Romans 10:17

So then faith cometh by hearing, and hearing by the word of God.

FILL IN THE BLANKS

1. Romans 10:17—__ then _____ cometh __ hearing, ___ hearing __ the ____ of ___.

2. _____—So ____ faith _____ by _____, and
_____ by ___ word ___ God.

3. Romans 10:17—So then faith cometh by hearing, _____.

4. Romans 10:17—_____, and hearing by the word
of God.

5. _____—So then faith cometh by hearing, and
hearing by the word of God.

6. Romans 10:17—_____

_____.

READ IT IN THE BIBLE

Find and read Romans 10:17 in your Bible.

WORD PUZZLE

Circle the hidden words in the puzzle below. Words may appear diagonally, vertically, horizontally, or backwards. Work puzzle in order as scripture is written here:

So then faith cometh by hearing, and hearing by the word of God.

```
H E A R I N G L
E A N D F O F M
A B D E D S A N
R W O R D I I O
I C C O M E T H
N E H T G J H P
G B Y B H K E Q
```

SAY THE WORD SCRAMBLE

Recite today's scripture again. As you do, cross off each of the words as they appear in the list below.

by word God hearing the of cometh faith So Romans 10:17 then by hearing and

PRAYING FROM GOD'S WORD

Pray for someone else right now, remembering that James 5:16 says, *"Pray one for another, that ye may be healed."*

YOUR THOUGHTS ON TODAY'S WORD

In the space below, write down what you have learned today as you meditate and dwell on our memory scripture.

_____

_____

_____

_____

EXTRA DAILY BIBLE READING

For an extra dose of God's Word, read Psalm 91 and Isaiah 54:17.

HEALING MEDICINE

Read the Healing Medicine that appears at the end of this chapter now and at least twice more today.

NOTES

_____
_____
_____
_____
_____
_____
_____
_____
_____
_____
_____

KEEPING THE FAITH

If suffering and affliction attempt to come upon you a second time, you can continue to rest and rely upon the powerful Word of God that has been planted in your heart! Keep planting. Keep reading the Word. Keep standing in faith that you will reap a harvest of blessing in your life!

RECITING TODAY'S SCRIPTURE

Slowly, say out loud three times ...

Nahum 1:9

Affliction shall not rise up the second time.

FILL IN THE BLANKS

1. Nahum 1:9—Affliction _____ not ____ up __ second ____.

2. _____—_____ shall ___ rise __ the _____ time.

3. Nahum 1:9—Affliction shall not _____.

4. Nahum 1:9—_____ rise up the second time.

5. _____—Affliction shall not rise up the second time.

154

6. Nahum 1:9—_____

_____.

READ IT IN THE BIBLE

Find and read Nahum 1:9 in your Bible.

WORD PUZZLE

Circle the hidden words in the puzzle below. Words may appear diagonally, vertically, horizontally, or backwards. Work puzzle in order as scripture is written here:

Affliction shall not rise up the second time.

```
A  F  F  L  I  C  T  I  O  N
S  H  A  L  L  R  I  Z  D  O
E  A  F  K  P  I  M  U  E  T
C  B  G  L  Q  S  E  P  F  H
O  C  H  M  R  E  W  A  G  E
N  D  I  N  S  U  X  B  H  J
D  E  J  O  T  V  Y  C  I  K
```

SAY THE WORD SCRAMBLE

Recite today's scripture again. As you do, cross off each of the words as they appear in the list below.

shall rise the second not Affliction up time Nahum 1:9

PRAYING FROM GOD'S WORD

Pray this prayer out of God's Word.

Father, in Jesus' name, I thank you that Jesus finished sickness and disease on the cross for me, and that affliction shall not rise up the second time.

(Nahum 1:9)

YOUR THOUGHTS ON TODAY'S WORD

In the space below, write down what you have learned today as you meditate and dwell on our memory scripture.

_____

_____

_____

EXTRA DAILY BIBLE READING

For an extra dose of God's Word, read Ezekiel 47:1–12, Revelation 22, and Ephesians 5:26.

HEALING MEDICINE

Read the Healing Medicine that appears at the end of this chapter now and at least twice more today.

NOTES

_____

_____

_____

_____

WEEK FOUR HEALING MEDICINE

Romans 10:10—*For with the heart man believeth unto righteousness; and with the mouth confession is made unto salvation.*

Mark 11:23—*That whosoever shall say unto this mountain, Be thou removed, and be thou cast into the sea; and shall not doubt in his heart, but shall believe that those things which he saith shall come to pass; he shall have whatsoever he saith.*

Mark 11:24—*Therefore I say unto you, What things soever ye desire, when ye pray, believe that ye receive them, and ye shall have them.*

Isaiah 41:10—*Fear thou not; for I am with thee: be not dismayed; for I am thy God: I will strengthen thee; yea, I will help thee; yea I will uphold thee with the right hand of my righteousness.*

II Timothy 1:7—*For God hath not given us the spirit of fear; but of power, and of love, and of a sound mind.*

Romans 10:17—*So then faith cometh by hearing, and hearing by the word of God.*

Nahum 1:9—*Affliction shall not rise up the second time.*

WEEK FOUR TEST

Congratulations! I hope you have learned a lot—and I pray that you will continue in God's Word. Now, I want you to again write down what you know about healing.

_____

_____

_____

_____

_____

Compare what you have written today with what you wrote on Day 1. Do you see the difference? We need to keep hiding His Word in our hearts. So, don't sit there and die, take hold of his Word each new day!

Fill In The Blanks

_____—*For with the heart man believeth unto righteousness; and with the mouth confession is made unto salvation.*

_____—*That whosoever shall say unto this mountain, Be thou removed, and be thou cast into the sea; and shall not doubt in his heart, but shall believe that those things which he saith shall come to pass; he shall have whatsoever he saith.*

_____—*Therefore I say unto you, What things soever ye desire, when ye pray, believe that ye receive them, and ye shall have them.*

_____—*Fear thou not; for I am with thee: be not dismayed; for I am thy God: I will strengthen thee; yea, I will help thee; yea, I will uphold thee with the right hand of my righteousness.*

_____—*For God hath not given us the spirit of fear; but of power, and of love, and of a sound mind.*

_____—*So then faith cometh by hearing, and hearing by the word of God.*

_____—*Affliction shall not rise up the second time.*

Romans 10:10_____

Mark 11:23—_____

Mark 11:24—_____

Isaiah 41:10—_____

II Timothy 1:7—_____

Romans 10:17—_____

Nahum 1:9—_____

MY PRAYER FOR YOU

I want to leave you with my prayer for you as you take all that you have learned and planted in your heart and live each new day. I pray that the Holy Spirit will always bring to your remembrance the powerful scriptures you have taken the time to sow into the garden of your heart. I pray that you will be quick to speak God's Word when faced with the trials of life that will surely come. I pray that you will continually lean on Jesus and all that He accomplished for us on the cross.

Most of all, I pray that your life would be a reflection of the love, faith, and joy that God has planted in your heart by the power of the Holy Spirit. May you awake each morning with a clear sense of His presence as you fulfill His destiny for your life!

ABOUT THE AUTHOR

Peggy Pennington Kirchhoff was born in California, and raised near Caddo Gap, Arkansas. A farm girl at heart, she married her childhood sweetheart Eddie. They have two children Jennifer and Craig, and five grandchildren. They have a very active family that does everything from kayaking to skydiving. Peggy lived most of her married life in Pampa, Texas (near Amarillo), where she taught EMT's for the local college. She loves thunderstorms, the woods and what it offers, the farm and being close to nature, a good book and the word of God. Peggy was once shut off from the activities of her very active family because of illness, but now is able to participate with her family and all the good things that go along with grandchildren. Peggy now lives in La Porte, Texas, on the Galveston Bay where she is active in her local church where she plans to teach and communicate the Word of God concerning healing. You can e-mail Peggy at pkirch-hoff@houston.rr.com, or call 281-479-1467.